WINGED ROCKETRY

BOOKS BY MAJOR
JAMES C. SPARKS, USAF (Ret.)

Rescue from the Air and in Space
Winged Rocketry

WINGED ROCKETRY

Major James C. Sparks
USAF (Ret.)

Illustrated with photographs

DODD, MEAD & COMPANY
New York

CREDITS FOR PHOTOGRAPHS

Bell Aircraft Corporation, 163, 164; Boeing Company, 146; Douglas Aircraft Company, Inc., 115, 116, 117; Lockheed Corporation, 166, 167, 168; Martin Company, 156, 158, 159; Martin Marietta Corporation, 159; National Aeronautics and Space Administration (NASA), 3, 138, 140, 141, 142, 148, 149, 150, 153, 171, 173, 177, 178, 179; Navy Department, The National Archives, 94, 98; Northrop Corporation, 151, 152, 154, 160; Michael Sparks, 15; Thiokol Chemical Corporation, 143; United States Air Force (USAF), 33, 34, 39, 42, 44, 45, 46, 48, 52, 56, 58, 60, 62, 64, 66, 68, 73, 74, 90, 95, 96, 97, 98, 101, 102, 103, 105, 106, 108, 111, 112, 113, 119, 120, 125, 127, 130, 133, 136, 138, 140, 155, 157; United States Air Force Archives, 13, 19, 25, 29, 47, 51, 75, 76, 78, 80, 85, 87; Wide World Photo, 9.

In memory of Joe Walker, Mel Apt, Ivan
Kincheloe, Skip Ziegler, and Major Michael
Adams, rocket pilots who tempted fate in
behalf of progress

CONTENTS

1

Man Is Wing-borne

Ever since man invented the most rudimentary forms of rocket propulsion, he has hoped to harness these discoveries to vehicles which would fly through the air. Legend has it that one early, would-be space voyager, an inventive man named Wan Hu, was considerably beyond his time in boldness. He was a minor Chinese official, probably the mayor of one of the ancient Chinese cities.

Wan Hu had observed children flying their kites during many of the traditional Chinese celebrations, such as New Year's Day, and he had always longed to emulate these flights—with himself on board.

This intrepid Chinaman's ambitions and thoughts were given great impetus by the invention of gunpowder, which had been put to work by Chinese warriors in the form of instruments of war called flaming arrows. Students of ancient China have determined that these arrows were simply what we know today as Roman-candle-type devices. The objective was not to propel these arrow-heads into the ranks of opposing soldiers, but, rather, to hurl a burning substance into the enemy fortifications which, in those days, were built of wood. These flaming devices also proved very effective against ships, whose riggings made excellent targets because of their susceptibility to fire. Unlike the conventional arrow fired from a bow, these arrows required no launching mechanism other than the simple, slow-burning devices attached to them. In his thoughts Wan Hu conceived what to him appeared to be an excellent way to propel man high into the air by blending the characteristics of the kite—which had been proven airworthy over and over again to his great satisfaction—and the simplicity of the rocket devices which had been used to hurl the flaming arrows into the fortifications of enemies. Hu pressed into service many of his workmen, building a vehicle which he was sure would give man the ability to break the bonds of earth's gravity, and fly.

Wan's plan called for the construction of a contraption which would employ a sedan chair as the cockpit of his strange craft. Behind the sedan chair he had coolies mount forty-seven rockets in a single cluster, strapped together with bamboo bands. To either side of the sedan chair would be attached large kites, actually enlarged versions of those he had seen the children fly during celebrations. These kites were held rigidly in place by an intricate web of bamboo structures.

The side of a rather steep hill was selected as the launching site for Hu's strange craft. The selection of this terrain was intended to give him the benefit of a little altitude, even at the time of launching. On the side of the hill he had constructed a launching ramp which was inclined at an angle of about twenty-five degrees. The ramp was waxed as a means of permitting the flight to leave with a minimum amount of friction, as the sedan chair sped off in its climb out at launching time.

Upon completion of his bizarre flying machine and the launching site, after much frenzied preparation Hu set a launching date. The countdown involved the services of about sixty coolies and Hu had meticulously rehearsed them many times in the ensuing weeks as a prelude to his momentous venture.

The count was to proceed in this fashion. Forty-seven of the coolies were to position themselves behind the sedan chair and stand ready with torches in hand. Two coolies were to hold the craft steady on either side as a means of stabilization for the takeoff run.

This X-15 rocket aircraft, looking like some strange giant crow, might startle the uninitiated of today as much as the legendary rocket craft of Wan Hu or the flying steam chariot of the Englishman, Charles Golightly, did in days gone by.

The remaining workers were just to be around in case they were needed to substitute for the others and to perform other related chores, such as waxing and polishing the track up which Wan would be propelled.

Finally the day arrived, and Hu sat in the weird structure, poised to make history as man's first space explorer. The coolies were assembled with military precision and they set about to make the necessary preparations. People gathered from miles around to witness this unbelievable venture. The countdown progressed according to the well-rehearsed plan. The kites were stabilized and made level with the launching ramp. The wax had been applied in abundance to permit a smooth run. All was ready. Wan Hu very pompously intoned the count on his own, when he had been assured that all other procedures had been completed. At the count of ten the coolies placed their torches in a fire which had been set at a previous point in the countdown. When they were all sure that they had a flame on the end of their torches, the latter were removed from the fire and held in readiness. The count progressed down the numerical scale—5-4-3-2-1-0. Upon reaching the zero mark, all forty-seven coolies put their torches to their assigned rocket fuses. The townspeople stood with bated breath. Then a cataclysmic explosion shook the mountainside. When the smoke subsided, only a large crater marked the spot where Wan Hu's first launching site had formerly stood—a very inauspicious beginning indeed for winged rocketry.

Although we will probably never know whether Wan Hu's exploits were fact or fantasy, we do know that many similarly "fantastic" ventures have been attempted with equal boldness. As long as man is able to dream and imagine and plan, he can, and has, developed machines which have overwhelmed the inventions of bygone eras. In his quest to mate the propulsive simplicity of the rocket with the envied ability of the birds, he has continued to work on the earth to be substantially prepared for the attempt in the air.

Many plans have been conceived, and for every thought which had some merit there were twenty which had no significance—other than, perhaps, their humorous moments of laughter, always a good antidote for frustration and weariness.

There were the periods of steam chariots and steam-propelled pigeons—replicas of birds made of wood. And there were steam reaction airplanes which were amazingly simple in principle and theoretically made sense. Take, for example, the patent sought in Britain by one Charles Golightly. Mr. Golightly conceived a plan for a figurative "steam horse," a train which he claimed could propel passengers from Paris to St. Petersburg in an hour or less. When Golightly was taken lightly in a cartoon in one of the leading newspapers of the day, the notoriety did nothing to enhance his stature. However, it did create much thought on the subject of propulsion and flying. The reaction engine harnessed to a flying machine again became a focal point of conversation. As a matter of fact, not only were such propulsive devices considered for machines of the air, but extensive thought was also given to their application to vehicles which would travel on the earth. Military engineers, in particular, considered the rocket engine for various roles—but to no practical avail.

All of the constructive thoughts and the sometimes ridiculous attempts to make unbelievably unorthodox machines take to the air were not entirely in vain, however, even though, on occasion, they were most discouraging to those who devoted so much time and effort to such ill-fated endeavors. On that momentous day, December 17, 1903, the ancient dream of man became a reality. Orville and Wilbur Wright actually flew in that medium which formerly had been denied to man. The feat was brought about through the power of, for its time, a rather complex engine. From this date forward aviation would travel at a phenomenal pace.

World War I gave aviation a great impetus. Airplanes of every description were built and flown in a very short period, in contrast to the earth-bound days which had gone before. But there were many who were not content to settle for the conventional airplane engine of the day. They believed that this device was rather crude in comparison to other means of propulsion which had already been demonstrated—namely, the rocket engine.

The end of the war in Europe brought about a vast reduction in the number of aircraft manufactured. But aviation boomed, nevertheless, in the form of barnstorming at county fairs and sports events, which served to whet the interest of the public in its future from the standpoint of commercial air travel. In Germany, aviation was brought to a standstill under the terms of the armistice, which forbade the Germans to engage in flying of any sort. This new vehicle—the airplane—a formidably destructive weapon system, had introduced a lethal dimension to warfare. The then war-prone Germans were most acutely aware of this, but they had to be content to explore flight-related activities in a very innocuous way. These formal restrictions in the more conventional avenues of aeronautical exploration probably account for the concentration on the more advanced field of flight. Some of those ventures might have had earth-shaking significance under proper leadership and more systematic channeling of experimentation, as will be described in later chapters.

In the mid-twenties there flourished in Germany an organization called the Society for Space Travel, which was devoted to the study of rockets, spaceships, and general topics related to space flight. Among the members of this group were men who ultimately would inscribe their names very indelibly in future space explorations—men such as Wernher von Braun, Dr. Herman Oberth, General Walter Dornberger, and many others of similar stature. Part of the Society's success seems to have been attributed to the fact that, since overtly no German could indulge in the field of aviation, those who had such inclinations could sublimate them by joining the Space Travel Society. Because so many sciences related to space travel were actually mere extensions of aviation, the Society became a natural vehicle for their interests and creative skills.

This was particularly true in the case of rocket propulsion. However, at that time most exponents did not conceive of rocket propulsion as having a direct practical application in the field of aviation, for they were acutely aware of the earliest rocket's many shortcomings. Rocket units in that era were capable of only a very few seconds of thrust and, so far, no way had been developed to throttle the engines and parcel out desired amounts of power. Nevertheless, all of this select group were aware of the long-range implications and the potentials of this type power plant which could push aircraft or missiles to still greater speeds and altitudes than those yet achieved.

Another facet of the environment in Germany which made it a breeding ground for inventive speculation was the fact that considerable theoretical thought could be devoted to the unconventional development of power plants for aircraft, thereby circumventing the restrictions imposed by the Geneva Convention. A particular loophole in these restrictions permitted the Germans to fly gliders, a sport which seemed to lend itself readily to the development of rocket engines, for the glider afforded an excellent test platform for the rocket. As one can recall, gliding became the major source of flying experience for the famed Luftwaffe at the beginning of World War II. However, the flight training had been carried on surreptitiously as a sports gliding program for German youth during the twenties and thirties. These graceful sail planes intrigued the Germans and the curious and adventurous nature of the young men and caused them to rally to it by the thousands.

There were no restrictions on rocket engine development, for at the time rockets were so simple by nature and definition that, on the surface, they appeared harmless in the international scheme of things. Who at the time could even remotely realize the awesome potential of such devices?

Consequently many Germans experimented with solid rocket

motors and used them to propel all sorts of vehicles, ranging from ice sleds to automobiles and, on occasion, even bicycles.

The most active of the European rocket group in the late twenties was Max Valier, who had a passion for speed and daring exploits in any form. He convinced one of Germany's most successful automobile manufacturers, Fritz von Opel, to underwrite the cost of building a rocket-propelled automobile as a publicity stunt. At first Von Opel queried Valier as to how long it would take to build such a vehicle, and the inventor assured him that they could take an existing car and harness to it the power of currently available powder rockets. The latter units were manufactured by a firm which specialized in rockets used for hurling lifelines to ships or persons in distress at sea. The owner of the firm, Frederick Sander, was so intrigued by their venture that he later became a participant financially and technically.

Sander's rocket units were unique in that he had developed a technique for compressing the powder to a much greater degree than other manufacturers, which resulted in superior performance. Valier and Sander talked over the project at great length and decided to use two different rockets as propulsive units for their first automobile. They would employ a solid and bored-type powder rocket in combination. The bored rockets would develop great thrust in short bursts, while the solid rockets would produce less thrust, but would burn for a considerably longer period.

After encountering several frustrating impediments, such as the refusal of the railroad authorities to ship their rocket units, the partners were finally able to conduct a very crude test. On March 15, 1928, they mounted one bored and one solid rocket on a small Opel automobile. A driver named Volckhart was engaged to carry out the first test. After days of meticulous preparation he got into the car, released the brakes, and ignited the rockets. The automobile moved off very sluggishly and coasted to a stop some 450 feet from the starting point.

Discouraged by so inept a performance, Opel was about to withdraw his offer. However, he was convinced by Sander in a last-minute plea that another attempt was in order because the poor performance was owing to the fact that the majority of the power was consumed in just moving the car off. Sander suggested that they accelerate the car with its own engine and cut in the rockets later. Again Volckhart was called upon for the driving chore. He started off in the car, using its conventional engine. After attaining a speed of around thirty miles per hour, he cut in the rockets. The car spurted ahead momentarily until he attained a speed of around forty-five miles per hour. The impressive thing about the experiment was the extremely short time interval required to attain the additional fifteen-miles-per-hour speed. Opel was willing to carry on with the experiments as a result of this run and he agreed to the construction of a special car for the purpose. Actually, the machine had the make-up of a conventional racing automobile, except that the engine had been removed. With the elimination of weight, experimenters could expect greater speeds. Six rocket units were attached to the rear of the vehicle. On April 11, 1928, the car was scheduled to make its first run. The rockets were ignited and all units came alive except one, which never fired. Nevertheless, the automobile was propelled down the track to a distance of around 2,000 feet. For the next run, eight rockets were attached to the racer. Again the driver attempted to fire them, and on this occasion one of them failed to ignite, and two others exploded. In spite of this, the car, undamaged, reached a speed of fifty-five miles per hour and traveled a distance of around 3,000 feet. Another test was scheduled for the following day. This time, twelve rockets were mounted on the uniquely powered automobile. Although five of the rockets did not ignite, the other seven propelled the car to a speed of more than seventy miles per hour.

The newspaper accounts of the event were glowing, and Opel was now very enthusiastic. He called a meeting of members of his engineering department and directed them to design a new car from the ground up. Such great aspirations were held for this vehicle that special stub wings were designed as a means of keeping it on the ground, for there was considerable apprehension that it might fly. After a short demonstration in it, conducted by Opel himself, on May 23, 1928, he chose to call the vehicle the Opel Rak (Opel

Rocket) II. Twenty-four rockets were used in this first speed run and all performed flawlessly. The car attained a speed of around 125 miles per hour. For the year 1928 this was truly an astounding speed, even for aircraft.

Opel was so impressed with the potential of the rocket engine mated to a racing automobile that he decided to build an even more daring performer. This one would be called the Opel Rak III, and instead of the wheels of a racing automobile, it would be equipped with railroad-car wheels and propelled down a track. In addition to the propellants in the rear, the car would have rockets in the front, to serve as brakes upon completion of the run. This was possibly the forerunner of the retrorockets used on spacecraft in present-day space flights. Certainly it was a practical demonstration of the use of rockets which had significant application later.

Opel was granted permission by the German government to use a stretch of railroad track, running between Burgwedel and Celle, two cities near Hanover. This particular section of track was selected because of its long, straight, and level characteristics. On June 23, 1928, the new rail car was fitted with ten rocket units. On this date, and for this trial at least, the vehicle was to make the run without a passenger. A clock mechanism would fire the rockets when a

One of the Fritz Von Opel racing automobiles, equipped with solid rocket engines. Note the wing-shaped airfoils mounted to the sides. These were intended to keep the automobile on the ground, particularly the front end, for there was some fear that it would actually fly.

short time interval had elapsed after starting. In addition, the timer was also set to fire the braking rockets at the end of the run. As witnesses waited intently, the timing device ticked off the seconds until it reached the moment of ignition. The rockets fired and the car leaped off with a high rate of acceleration, rapidly attaining a speed of around 180 miles per hour.

Spurred on by the early success of Rak III, Von Opel had the car towed back to the starting point for another attempt. This time his crewmen fitted thirty rockets to the mounting racks of the unusual machine. It was to be the go-for-broke attempt as far as the test crews were concerned, and they had great hopes for success. The automatic timer ticked off the seconds until ignition, and the car again leaped off to an uncertain future. The acceleration was so violent that the car literally flew off the tracks, careening wildly out of control until it was completely demolished.

Undismayed, Von Opel and his crew set about building the Opel Rak IV. This automobile met a similar fate to that of the Rak III, and by this time the railroad officials had begun to take a dim view of the explosive violence of the experiments, which had been occurring on their stretch of track. Although Von Opel had ordered the building of the fifth in the series of rocket cars, the railroad executives, sensing more difficulties, stepped in and forbade him to test it on their tracks. This terminated the experiments with the racing cars.

As so frequently occurs with unorthodox experimenters who, when thwarted on the one hand, divert their energies to new endeavors, Von Opel, Sander, and Valier were not the type of men to retire from challenges merely because one substantial roadblock had been placed in their way. Actually, the fact that the railroad officials blocked the further use of the company's tracks for their speed trials was, in the long run, a source of good, for it diverted the experimenters to new ventures with more productive significance.

Frederick Stamer, who manufactured the solid rockets for the racing cars, was filled with the idea of harnessing the power of the rocket motor to an aircraft of one shape or another. In conjunction with a brilliant young aeronautical engineer, Alexander Lippisch, the dauntless Stamer designed a glider with the sole intention of mating it to solid rockets. The ultimate aim of the pair was to perfect a means of propelling gliders to altitudes economically. This would have a great impact on the sport of gliding.

The final design of their glider was the result of experimentation with models which were fitted with scaled-down rocket power plants, depending upon their size. On several occasions the models met with less than success. Some accelerated so rapidly on takeoff that their wings were sheared off. This was one of the hazards with which the inventors had to contend, since solid rockets could not be throttled and their inherent characteristic was rapid burning; hence, rapid acceleration and the resultant high-gravity forces. Fritz von Opel, although not an active participant at this point, was financing the venture. A German glider club had offered to make a glider available for the experiments. The site for this historic adventure was in the Rhon Mountains, one of the favorite spots in Germany for gliding enthusiasts.

The date selected for the first flight was June 11, 1928, and Stamer was to be the pilot. He decided to start off very conservatively with the rocket units, and progressively work up to larger increments of power. In addition, he intended to use a rope in the first launching, to assist in getting him air-borne. The results of the flight can best be summed up in the report which Stamer wrote shortly after it was completed. "The plane took to the air by means of a rubber rope, aided by one rocket (brander). After flying for about 200 yards in a straight line, I noticed a slight climb. I made a curve of about forty-five degrees to the right and flew another 300 yards. Then I turned to the right again about forty-five degrees. Immediately after the second turn, the first rocket ceased burning and I ignited the second. This time I flew about 500 yards in a straight line, made a turn to the right of about thirty degrees, and landed the machine after another 200 meters, just a few seconds before the second rocket was exhausted."

The flight lasted just over a minute and covered a distance of little more than a mile. Stamer reported that the flight had been "extremely pleasant" and added, "I had the impression of merely soaring; only the loud hissing sound reminded me of the rockets."

For his second flight, Stamer intended to fly over one of the local mountains. Again quoting from Stamer's flight report, the event went as follows: "The launching went all right and while the plane took to the air I ignited the first rocket. After one or two seconds it exploded with a loud noise. The nine pounds of powder were thrown out and ignited the plane instantly. I let it drop for some sixty feet to tear the flames off. After succeeding in that I landed the plane without mishap."

Just after Stamer landed, another rocket unit caught fire but, fortunately for the occupant, it did not explode. The glider was in need of rather extensive repair.

The gliding society which loaned Stamer the glider had not just indulged in a benevolent gesture by permitting him the use of their aircraft for these experiments. They had reasoned that if he could develop a practical way to launch gliders by means of rockets, it would simplify their major problem—the need to employ several men to assist in getting one glider air-borne. Concrete success in the experiment would have been a real boon to their sport. Another advantage would be the elimination of the rubber ropes and automobiles now used for the launchings. As matters now stood after the second flight, they were not impressed and they refused Stamer any future use of the club's gliders.

From the Gliding Society in the Rhon Mountains, Stamer and Von Opel turned to other sources for collaboration in their flying efforts. The Raab-Katzenstein Aircraft Company of Kassel built a new glider considerably larger than the one used in the two earlier flights. The experiments that followed were all disappointing, however, both to the manufacturer and to Stamer and Von Opel, and they were terminated.

Although Stamer, who had had more than his share of frustrating experiences—along with some successes—chose to give up at this point, Von Opel was equally determined to carry on and he had a new glider constructed which he intended to fly on September 30, 1929. This glider was delivered for flight testing. Unlike the setup for the earlier attempts, Von Opel had constructed a special takeoff

The rocket-equipped glider of Fritz Von Opel, the automobile industrialist, marked the first significant effort in the harnessing of rocket power for use in propelling flying machines. Von Opel barely escaped with his life during this particular flight.

ramp—actually a single wooden track, about seventy feet in length. He planned to use no special launching devices to assist him in getting off the ramp. He would fly off under the power of the rocket motors which he carried on board.

Two attempts were made prior to noon on the thirtieth, and both times the glider came to an abrupt and rather inglorious stop after dropping off the end of the launching track. Obviously, the rocket units were not generating enough power to get the craft air-borne. Von Opel had various combinations of rockets strapped to the rugged little glider and, finally, in midafternoon he got off the ramp and into the air. The flight lasted about ten minutes and he attained a speed of around 100 miles per hour. The combination of the relatively high landing speed of the craft and its weight was not conducive to the aircraft staying intact, and it was rather badly damaged upon landing. In addition, one of the wings caught fire in mid-air. This resulted, unfortunately, in the demise of the aircraft which had just made a special mark in history by performing the first rocket-powered takeoff. It would never fly again. People who observed the afternoon event said it was miraculous that Von Opel came out of the accident unscathed. This put an end to Von Opel's contribution to the rather precarious avocation of rocket airplane flying.

Meanwhile, Max Valier had also given up his efforts with the gliders and decided to devote his time to the development of a new propulsive unit for racing automobiles. He had been made well aware of the shortcomings of the solid-rocket motor in his experiences with racing cars. These motors burned for only short durations; consequently, they could not generate sufficient prolonged thrust to accelerate to higher speeds.

Valier was convinced that only an engine utilizing liquid oxygen and gasoline could meet the requirements of such a power plant, and he set out to construct one. He fitted his completed unit to a racing car. Witnesses say that, on the first run, a billowing reddish flame, along with sluggish black smoke, poured from the rear of the unit, which signaled poor or incomplete combustion. Undismayed by the initial performance, he carefully probed the causes of his failure and attempted to remedy them. He particularly wanted to correct the problems with his liquid rocket engine in time to prepare the car for a performance during "Aviation Week"—a week-long show which featured new scientific and technical novelties, along, of course, with aircraft. This event meant the gathering in Berlin of the elite of aviation, space, and scientific personalities. He was sure that his racing car would be the major attraction at this affair and he was particularly eager to make a run in front of so esteemed a group.

In his great desire to get the vehicle ready, Valier worked very long and late at the factory with which he was associated. The new firm was called the Association for the Utilization of Industrial Gases. On Saturdays there were no distractions, since it was an off day for everyone else. This particular Saturday had been quite productive. He made several test runs with the rocket engine, but without letting the car move. During what could have been the last run he had planned for the day, he let the engine idle in order to get some indication of the smoothness of combustion. As he stood nearby, with his ear tuned to the deep roar of the power plant, suddenly and without warning it exploded, probably because of excessive pent-up back pressure caused by the idling. A large splinter of the mechanism was propelled into his body, severing a major blood vessel. He bled to death on the floor of the factory. Max Valier, the man who had challenged danger on the auto race tracks and in the air, became the world's first victim of rocket research. Although he did not live to see his dreams come true, his efforts have not been in vain. They have given impetus to many in the field, and particularly to young people who have followed his bold experiments with racing cars and gliders.

The two remaining notables in European circles who made attempts to use the rocket engine on automobiles and gliders—Von Opel and Stamer—disappeared from the scene and were seldom heard from again.

Many people, and especially some of the more conservative members of the scientific community, thought that these three did more harm than good to gain acceptance of the rocket as a means of propulsion. The fact remains, however, that because of their unorthodox approaches and their lack of inhibition they probably indulged in concrete dramatic events and experiments which never would have occurred if left to the theoreticians. They were boldly imaginative men, and the greatest asset associated with their colorful adventures was the inspiration which they conveyed to those yet to come. They had hurled man into the skies on the thrust of wing-borne rockets. As a result, rocket research boomed the world over.

Charles Golightly, an Englishman, invented a steam chariot which, he claimed, would fly from Paris to Russia.

2

The Dawn of a New Era

One of those on whom Valier's experiments had made an indelible impression was a young man named Wernher von Braun. He had read and followed the exploits of Max Valier while still in his teens, and he was convinced that this new field of rocket propulsion was for him.

After college he was hired by—then Captain and later General— Walter Dornberger, to conduct research on the use of rockets as a substitute for artillery for the German Army.

One of the earliest projects assigned to Von Braun in his new job was the development of a primitive rocket engine which used liquid oxygen and alcohol as a fuel mixture. His thoughts, however, began to wander from the task assigned to him. He was convinced that an engine similar to the one which was in the throes of being built, could propel an aircraft, not just of the glider class, but a conventional airplane which would normally fly by means of ordinary internal-combustion engines. Ironically, he had already tried to interest the Germany Army, his current employer, in his experiment, but to no avail. He then tried the Air Force, which was usually noted for bold technical ventures. Again there was nothing but disdain for his concept. Finally, he chanced to meet Ernst Heinkel, a German industrialist and manufacturer of some of the foremost aircraft of the world in that period. Von Braun told Heinkel of his plan and the latter responded with a very attentive ear. He even agreed to make available to the young scientist the fuselage of a Heinkel-112 fighter. Von Braun was to try to mate his engine to the Heinkel design as a preliminary to a future flyable craft.

Heinkel assigned other engineers and several highly qualified riggers to assist Von Braun. The next step was to find a test pilot for such a bold undertaking. The lethal nature of rocket engines in that period and the untimely demise of Valier prompted much serious thought on the part of Von Braun in his quest for a suitable test pilot. After looking over the records of many prospective candidates, and inquiring among his friends and professional acquaintances, he decided on a bachelor named Eric Warsitz, a lieutenant in the Luftwaffe. The fact that Warsitz had no family played a large part in the final selection, for all associated with the project knew that this was to be a very precarious flying venture indeed.

After the assignment of Warsitz to the project, the team made strides in installing the engine in the fuselage of the near-wingless fighter plane. The first tests were merely to prove that the power unit would work inside the fuselage of the aircraft. In order to accomplish this, the technicians would have to mount the alcohol tank behind the pilot's seat and the liquid oxygen tank in front of it. This was a most critical engineering problem, for if the two ingredients got together inadvertently, the results would be catastrophic. As a matter of fact, the fuel that the Von Braun engine used is classified as hypergolic, which means that when its ingredients are brought together in a combusion chamber, ignition occurs on contact. Hence, the system does not require a spark plug or any electrical ignition for operation.

On the day of the first test run, Von Braun and his crew jacked up the tail of the airplane and aligned the fuselage parallel to the ground. This was done to keep the exhaust gases from being driven toward the ground, thereby avoiding any possible misreadings of their thrust output measurements. The wheels were anchored very securely to the ground, to prevent the airplane from rolling when the engine was started.

As a safety precaution, Von Braun had a concrete bunker built adjacent to the aircraft, which not only served as an observation post, but, most importantly, he had installed remote controls inside. With these, he could start and guide the engine from a safe shelter. After several successful engine runs, Von Braun and Warsitz had developed enough confidence in the apparatus to stand on the stubby wings during one of the tests. Other than the inability to hear for a few minutes after the engine run-up periods, they were none the worse for wear as a result of the experiments.

Von Braun continued to improve his rocket engine through the redesign of certain parts, but he had considerable trouble with the combustion chamber. The latter would get so hot during test operations that the metal would give way and it would disintegrate. Temperatures in the chamber frequently soared to more than 1,000 degrees and the metals he was using were incapable of withstanding such intense heat.

In one of these tests, the complete rocket unit blew up. The explosion was so violent that it destroyed the entire airplane. Undiscouraged, Heinkel furnished the experimental group with a replacement. After several test runs, this airplane met the same fate. However, Von Braun, not prone to discouragement, at this point felt that he had gained sufficient knowledge to rule out any similar occurrences in the future, and he asked for another fighter plane. This time he obtained a complete and flyable aircraft. Again he mounted one of his improved engines in the tail. After a series of trial runs on the ground, he informed Lieutenant Warsitz that the little craft was ready for the first test flight.

While making preparations for the shakedown flight, the pair started their routine engine run-up. During this operation Warsitz had to watch an instrument which would indicate the pressures in the oxygen and alcohol tanks. When they reached a certain figure, he would pull a lever and permit the fuels to flow into the combustion chamber. The latter could withstand only about half a minute of such pressures. Just as they were about to commit the airplane to its first flight, the unit exploded, hurling Warsitz from the cockpit. Fortunately, and miraculously, he escaped unharmed,

The first aircraft other than a glider to fly by means of rocket power was the Heinkel 112 fighter, shown above. The propulsive unit mounted in the rear of the fuselage generated over 2,000 pounds of thrust. Flights were conducted with the propeller and the rocket engine working in unison and also with rocket power alone.

but the aircraft was destroyed.

With lurking doubts in their minds as to his receptiveness, Von Braun and Warsitz went back to see Heinkel in an effort to obtain still another aircraft. With so much time and effort tied up in the experiments at this point, Heinkel felt obliged to see the project through and, to their vast relief, he consented to give them another aircraft.

About a month went by while Von Braun and Warsitz made feverish preparations to prove that a rocket aircraft could fly. Finally, after overcoming many seemingly insurmountable hurdles, Warsitz climbed into the cockpit of the little fighter with the strange object protruding from its tail and took off under power of the piston-driven engine.

After climbing to what he considered to be a safe and proper altitude for the test, he began to pressurize the tanks of the rocket engine. He maneuvered the airplane into a straight and level course and the craft settled down to a speed of around 190 miles per hour. When he was convinced that all was ready, he switched on the rocket engine. The fighter lurched ahead abruptly, accelerating in scant seconds to around 250 miles per hour. But at this moment trouble developed. Fumes poured into the cockpit and began to stifle the pilot. To compound his already precarious position, the heat began to rise to an unbearable temperature. Convinced that the airplane was in imminent danger of exploding, he unbuckled his seat belt and prepared to bail out. However, after looking at his altimeter and, more importantly, at the ground below, he made an instinctive decision to ride it down. As he was aligning the fighter with the field, in preparation for a landing, a new dilemma suddenly confronted him. The landing gear would not come down! Since there was no other alternative, he put the plane down gently on the fuselage, with the wheels up. The flashing blades of the propellers chewed up chunks of the earth while he skidded to a stop. He hastily bounded out of the craft as flames sprang from its tail. Fortunately, a well-disciplined ground crew moved in and doused the fire before it got out of control.

Eric Warsitz was jubilant, in spite of his harrowing escape from danger just moments before. Thoughts of his near-tragic end were soon lost in the exhilaration of being the first man on earth to fly an airplane powered by a liquid rocket engine.

Warsitz promptly went over the machine with meticulous care, assisted by his engineering crew, to see if they could determine the cause of the trouble. After considerable investigation, they decided that faulty exhaust vents had permitted fuel to seep into the cockpit area.

Having found the cause of the fire, the crew hastily restored the aircraft to a flyable condition. Warsitz took to the air again and made a series of flights, all without serious incident. These flights were all made by taking off with the fighter's regular reciprocal engine. The rocket engine was cut in as soon as a safe altitude had been reached. After several more flights, Warsitz had acquired enough confidence in the craft to try a takeoff with rocket power only. This was to be the climax of their efforts and the entire group fairly exuded enthusiasm.

The time was the summer of 1937 and, although the project was going well, Heinkel and Warsitz were greatly disappointed that the German Air Ministry had not shown greater interest in the rocket-propelled airplane project. Undismayed, they felt that, in some way, their efforts would not go unnoticed forever, and they made the aircraft ready for what would be the last of the experiments.

The pilot, whose bearing radiated confidence in his ability to fly unusual airplanes, climbed into the cockpit. He strapped himself in and confirmed to the ground crew that all was ready. With a wave to those standing by, he fired up the rocket engine and the little fighter moved off without a hitch, a comet-like stream of fire spurting from the tail. The rocket engine was brought to full thrust, then cut out after it had burned all of its fuel, which happened in mere seconds. Immediately, Warsitz put the plane into a shallow dive to maintain his air speed and glided back to the air strip. There he made a smooth landing. Again this intrepid pilot had made aeronautical history by flying an airplane by means of liquid rocket power alone, including the takeoff.

While Von Braun, Heinkel, and Warsitz had been in the throes of successfully flying the Heinkel-112, with Von Braun's engine, another brilliant engineer, Helmut Walter, of Keil, in northern Germany, had been conducting independent research on a rocket engine. Walter, however, had not given any thought to the use of his engine in aircraft. Instead, probably influenced by his proximity to the large seaport town of Keil, he had developed his engine for use in submarines. The idea was that the rocket engine would work ideally under water. Since the innate characteristics of a rocket engine rule out the need for fuel ingredients, which must come from external sources, he figured that his apparatus would be well suited to the needs of the submarine, where everything must also be self-contained.

Unlike the Von Braun engine, which used alcohol and liquid oxygen, Walter's engine employed hydrogen peroxide and a mixture of methanol water and hydrazine. Also, the operating characteristics of the latter engine were quite different from those of the Von Braun unit. The flame in the rocket's tail was practically invisible, in contrast with that produced by the engine which propelled the little Heinkel fighter. This glowed with a more pronounced orange hue. Such a glow is indicative of poor combustion in any engine that operates with petroleum fuel and oxygen in combination. In every type of rocket engine, the speed of the gases as they exit from the nozzle determines the thrust of the engine. In the oxygen-petroleum-fueled engine a more effective combustion is indicated as the color of the flame moves to the blue or white spectrum.

The Walter engine obviously had achieved a higher degree of reliability than the Von Braun engine, although it had not yet been harnessed to a useful vehicle of any sort. To prove its practicality, the Walter unit was installed in the same Heinkel fighter plane that had previously flown with the Von Braun unit attached. After a series of tests, it was proved beyond doubt that the Walter engine was relatively simple, efficient, and reliable.

This good word traveled rapidly to influential members of the Air Ministry. Their curiosity was now definitely aroused. However, their interest lay in a different vein from that advocated by Von Braun, Heinkel, and Warsitz. Most of the interested members seemed to consider that the rocket's greatest value lay in the field of auxiliary units, to assist in the takeoff of heavily laden bombers and transports.

It was to this end that several Walter units were ordered by the Air Ministry for experimental purposes. The test aircraft for these units was to be a Heinkel 111 bomber, to which special mounts were fitted for accommodating the takeoff devices. The ground crewmen promptly labeled them the "power eggs." The test bomber was loaded with cargo in excess of its normal ability to lift off the ground, and actual runs were made to ascertain whether the calculated takeoff weight limits with the bomber's regular engines were valid. This proved to be the case. The aircraft would not break ground in trial runs.

Next, the crew tried a takeoff with the Walter units. The lumbering and overladen aircraft moved out slowly until the rockets were fired. As the smoke poured from the two power packs, the aircraft leaped off the earth with amazing climbing ability, although its weight was in excess of its ability even to become air-borne with normal engines. A definite case had been made for the use of the auxiliary power units on bombers and cargo planes.

Although the demonstration of Walter's auxiliary power unit was a complete success, Heinkel, Warsitz, and Von Braun were still convinced that the future of the rocket engine in aeronautics lay in its ability to improve the speed and climbing characteristics of fighter aircraft. Ironically, no one from the Air Ministry at this point in time shared their enthusiasm with regard to rocket-powered fighter aircraft.

With, or without, formal endorsement of the Air Ministry, Herr Heinkel and his creative group decided that they would go it alone, and advance the development of rocket fighters. Heinkel called the group together and asked what they thought of building a rocket fighter themselves from the ground up. This would not be just a propeller-driven fighter converted for research purposes with a makeshift rocket engine in the tail. Heinkel was thinking of the world's first pure rocket aircraft. He knew the answer to his question prior to asking it, for the entire group rallied with great enthusiasm when he broached the topic. This ingenious collection of aeronautical talent became involved in a lively design session. Their ideas ran the design gamut as to how the airplane should be built and along what lines.

The initial concern was the best size for such an airplane. This was very important, for a large craft would permit them to build in greater safety features for the benefit of Warsitz, who would also be test flying this revolutionary new bird. The pilot sensed that the designers were going out of their way to focus the major consideration of their plans on concern for his safety. He thereupon took his turn on the floor and discussed the merits of designing the smallest possible airplane—and with good logic. His major argument was that it would make more sense to build a small airplane because power plants were available at that moment which could propel a lighter experimental craft to the speed which they desired to attain —about 1,000 kilometers per hour (between 550 and 600 miles per hour). A larger airplane would require a more powerful propulsion unit, which would mean a lengthy period of waiting until the latter could be built. Warsitz reminded his audience that the most basic aerodynamic theory dictates that the larger a body is, the more drag it encounters as it moves through the air stream, and the smaller a body is, the less drag it must overcome.

Obviously, the group was relieved to hear their test pilot confirm that he was in favor of building the smaller aircraft, since he was destined to be the man to fly it. The die was cast, and they all agreed they would build a small—but one large enough—airplane to fit Warsitz, who at six feet two was certainly no midget.

When they were deciding on the size of the rocket plane in their earliest discussions, little did they realize just how small the aircraft would actually be when it was finally constructed. Its wings were a mere sixteen feet from tip to tip, and the fuselage was of a comparable dimension, being only twenty-four inches at the broadest point, and a scant three feet from floor to ceiling. The pilot's seat had to be tilted in order to accommodate a man of Warsitz's physical stature. This became the basis of much good-natured kidding by the ground crew. They would say such things as "Don't take your wallet along today or you won't be able to sit upright in the cockpit."

Another major hurdle which the ingenious gathering of designers had to surmount was the fact that, even with the HE-112 fighter, the addition of the rocket engine brought about a situation where the usual flight instruments were insufficient to meet the demands of greater speed, a faster rate of climb, and an altitude potential far in excess of that known for the conventional aircraft of the day. This meant that, in addition to building a higher-performance aircraft, they would have to devise revolutionary new instruments as well.

In spite of Warsitz's willingness to take the risk of flying an aircraft with such an unusual performance potential, the governing group insisted that every effort be made to give him the maximum chance for survival. Building safety devices into this aircraft led to the development of various contrivances which would eventually find a permanent place in aeronautical construction. For instance, at the speed at which Warsitz would be flying, there would be absolutely no chance for him to bail out of the fighter in a conventional manner. The most significant of the innovations designed especially for this aircraft was the arrangement whereby the entire canopy housing the pilot would be blown free of the rest of the

Three views of the Heinkel 176, the world's first aircraft to be equipped only with rocket power. It flew for the first time on June 20, 1939, at Peenemunde, a site which became the research center for Germany's arsenal of futuristic weapons.

airplane in case of trouble. The mechanism was actuated by compressed air, and hundreds of tests were conducted to prove its effectiveness. This research ultimately led to the development of the ejection seat, which was adopted later by the Luftwaffe in World War II, and ultimately by all air forces for use in high-performance fighters and bombers.

One of the features of the airplane's design which was undesirable, but essential in keeping the construction simple, was the placement of the landing gear in the fuselage, instead of in the wings. Such an arrangement meant that the wheels of the front landing gear would be only two feet apart. This made landing and takeoff so precarious, especially in cross winds, that wing-tip skids were installed as a safety measure.

In the summer of 1938, the airplane finally was completed and was commissioned the Heinkel-176. Being a better performer than its crude predecessor, the HE-112, it could not be flown at the same field. Since there had been stepped-up interest in rocketry—and in aeronautics in general—shown by the Air Ministry, and the German army, recently, arrangements were made for the unique craft to be flown at a newly-activated site called Peenemunde. Few people realized at the time that developments at this facility ultimately would stun the world and introduce a revolutionary new military technology into Germany's arsenal.

The HE-176 was crated and transported to Peenemunde by truck. After the reassembly of the wings, which had been removed for the trip to the airfield, the craft was made ready for taxi tests within two days. These tests were carried out in a most unusual fashion.

A supercharged Mercedes, which was the fastest commercially produced automobile in Germany at that time, was bought and modified for use in towing the HE-176. The group sought out one of northern Germany's smoothest beaches, on which to conduct the high-speed towing tests, and transferred the aircraft there. During the trial runs that followed, Warsitz sat in the cockpit at the controls, while the Mercedes driver towed him down the beach at speeds of more than 100 miles per hour. Owing to the softness and irregular structure of the sand, compounded by the narrowness of the landing gear, the tests became so precarious that they had to be abandoned. Warsitz decided to return to Peenemunde with the HE-176 and use the rocket engine itself for the taxi trials.

The Walter unit had been progressively improved while the HE-176 was in the process of construction and, as a result, the model which had been fitted to the airplane developed around 1,100 pounds of thrust. On the day Warsitz had the aircraft towed out to the runway for the first powered taxi run, he pointed the stubby craft down the long strip and pushed forward on the throttle. The little fighter shot forward with amazing acceleration. He had to retard the throttle quickly lest he take to the air before he really acquired a feel for the untried machine. After several rocket-powered short spurts down the long runway, Warsitz's confidence began to build, for he had acquired the feel of the airplane. Next in the chain of events, the HE-176 would be lifted from the runway, but only for very short intervals, and only two or three feet above the strip.

As the tests progressed, the hops became longer and longer, until the maximum distance had been obtained—unless extensions were made to the runway. This took time, but the improvements were essential to their plans, and Warsitz did not want to take unnecessary risks—but not because of any personal fear of the airplane. He considered the little fighter too valuable a commodity to smash up recklessly. He felt that too much time and effort had already been expended to risk changing the established pattern of orderly testing of the craft. When the runway extensions were completed, the speed and altitude of the short hops were increased.

On June 30, 1939, as war clouds lurked over Europe, Eric Warsitz pressed forward on the throttle of the strange flying machine and it leaped effortlessly into the air. The flight lasted for only a mere fifty to fifty-five seconds, but another milestone had been crossed in aviation, for the first pure rocket-powered aircraft had been flown.

Swept away in jubilation over a successful first flight, Warsitz made contact with ranking members of the German Air Ministry that evening and invited them over to Peenemunde to witness a demonstration the following day.

Everyone associated with the project expected great enthusiasm for their aeronautical oddity. Instead, the Air Ministry officials joked and made very condescending remarks about the unorthodox craft. Colonel Udet, a famous German flier and then chief of Technical Research for the Air Ministry, quipped, "Lieutenant Warsitz, do you want to fly with that? Why, it's got no wings. Those things look more like a pair of steps."

Warsitz gave no outward indication of being perturbed by such comments, for at this time he had more to worry about than mere flippancies from disinterested bureaucrats. The weather in the Peenemunde area was fast deteriorating and he was apprehensive that a snarl in the flight plan at this point could really sabotage any future there might be for so revolutionary an aeronautical venture.

Although Warsitz had to take off in a slight cross wind, which made the airplane weave and rock from side to side as it gathered speed, the flight went off successfully. Milch, the ranking member of the Air Ministry, promoted him to captain on the spot, after landing, and Udet shook the pilot's hand warmly. However, to the utter amazement of the entire group, Udet announced that the project would be stopped and that he was forbidding any further flights.

Warsitz protested Udet's decision, pleading for him to hear of the future plans of the experimenters for the HE-176. It took several follow-up trips to Berlin before the test pilot could convince the official to let the program go on. Several flights were made in the ensuing days and they were longer in duration than any previous attempts. Then from out of the blue a telephone call came from Udet to Warsitz, during which he requested that the rocket plane be grounded and that no further flights or modifications be made. The reason for the grounding order, the group found out later, was that there was to be a special demonstration of new aircraft staged for Hitler during the first week of July in Berlin, and that the German Air Ministry wanted the HE-176 to fly in the exhibition. This certainly seemed a little incongruous in light of the lack of enthu-

In addition to building power plants for fighter aircraft, the Germans also developed rocket units to assist heavily laden bomber aircraft to take off from short fields. The units were called "power eggs," because of their physical resemblance to eggs, and were slung beneath the engine nacelles. They were dropped as soon as the fuel supply had been spent.

siasm shown earlier by Udet.

Hitler and his entourage arrived in Berlin on the third of July and they made the rounds of the aircraft exhibits and watched some of the flying demonstrations. Hitler was obviously interested in the HE-111 bomber, which led off the show with a demonstration of a short-field takeoff, using the auxiliary rocket-power units which had been developed by the Walter firm. He stood with rapt attention as the huge machine trundled out to the runway. An identical aircraft, except for the absence of rocket units, was slated to take off simultaneously as a means of contrasting the performance of airplanes with the two types of propulsion. This arrangement proved the experimenters' points, for the rocket-equipped aircraft, although now heavily laden, moved off rapidly and was more than 500 feet out in front of the one with the conventional piston engine, even on the takeoff roll.

Later in the day, Hitler arrived with his group beside the HE-176. He gave the little craft a cursory inspection as some of his ill-informed staff members tried to describe the objectives of the rocket airplane. After a few necessary amenities for protocol's sake, Warsitz squeezed his six-foot frame into the tiny cockpit, ignited the rocket, and moved out across the field. The ground crew drew a sigh of relief as the winged blowtorch lifted from the runway. Warsitz circled the field above the inspection group, with the engine off. He had deliberately held back some fuel in order to demonstrate the fact that the engine could be restarted in flight. Just as he was over the heads of the gathering, he fired up the power plant with an impressive roar, circled once more, and then came in for a landing, touching down at a speed of around 200 miles per hour.

Hitler, in a curious gesture, sent one of his aides over to the HE-176 in the official car to pick up Warsitz. Upon his arrival back at the flight ramp, Hitler warmly shook the pilot's hand. At the same time he turned to Heinkel and asked how much he had paid Warsitz for the flight. Heinkel responded with a figure—and hastily added that this was in addition to the pilot's Luftwaffe pay, for Warsitz was really on loan to the Heinkel factory, to work on such projects. However, it was completely legal for Heinkel to pay the man an additional salary because of the extreme risks he was taking.

The aides all converged on Warsitz, to compliment him on the success of the amazing machine and its flight. But they appeared to be rather empty gestures, and the pilot sensed that they were made only in response to Hitler's presence.

Goering asked Warsitz rather flippantly what he thought of the future of such an airplane. Without hesitation, the test pilot replied, "Herr General Field Marshal, I am convinced that in a year or two from now very few military aircraft will have propellers and piston engines." Goering responded, "You're an optimist, aren't you?" with a note of sarcasm in his voice. As a parting gesture, Goering did order an aide to have a special payment of 20,000 marks made to Warsitz for the day's flying exhibition.

Warsitz later told Heinkel of meetings which were held in Berlin, during which it became rather obvious that Hitler's underlings did not understand the ramifications of such development work and that they somehow saw the whole endeavor as a joke or the creation of an aeronautical oddity.

Warsitz and Heinkel, sensing a very dubious outlook for the future of their rocket plane, turned now to another aircraft which they had been developing in secrecy but whose flying timetable trailed that of the HE-176. This venture would also have earth-shaking implications, for it was destined to become the world's first jet aircraft and, through it, Warsitz would add another laurel to his ever-growing list of flying adventures. He would go on to become the pilot of the world's first jet aircraft, the HE-178.

With Germany on the brink of war, it is difficult to comprehend how such sophisticated and promising experimentation could have been treated so lightly by ranking German officials. Their country's loss of time in acquiring a great offensive power through their neglect of so ambitious an air weapon is incalculable. As the RAF by night, and the American Air Force by day, ruled the skies over Germany, there must have been many anguished moments among those who could have, yet failed, to give impetus to this program which could have such a significant bearing on the outcome of the war. Truly, many of the sleepless nights endured by the German hierarchy were of their own making—fortunately for the side of the Allies.

3

The Fighter That Could
Have Changed the War

On August 19, 1944, a critical period in World War II, a secret message went out to the commanding officers of all the subordinate commands of the Eighth Air Force stationed in England. Although transmitted in rather matter-of-fact language, this caused considerable apprehension and concern behind the scenes for the subject covered in the letter was of the utmost military importance. The contents of the message were as follows:

19 August 1944

SUBJECT: German Jet Propelled Aircraft

TO   : Commanding Officers, All Stations, Eighth Air Force

1. For about the past nine years, German aeronautical engineers have been experimenting with propulsion units other than internal combustion engines, and it is believed that aircraft employing the jet principle were being developed by Junkers, Messerschmitt and Hirth (a Heinkel subsidiary) as far back as 1941.

2. At present, five aircraft, the ME-163, ME-262, HE-280, DO-335 and AR-234 are reported to be in production. Of these, it appears that the jet types developed by the Messerschmitt firm have proven the most successful and that current production activity is being con-

This reconnaissance photograph shows the airstrip at Peenemunde, Germany, where jet and rocket aircraft were first sighted. Note bomb craters among buildings. Since the airfield was primarily for research and development and not an active Luftwaffe interception base, the facilities were considered more important as a target than the runway itself.

centrated on the single unit, ME-163, and the twin unit, ME-262. PRU coverage first revealed the ME-163 at Peenemunde in the summer of 1943, and the ME-262 at Lechfield early this year. Recent aerial sighting reports indicate that both these aircraft are now being introduced into operation.

3. So far, little verified information is available on the enemy's jet propelled aircraft. The main source for performance data and construction features has been PW's (prisoners of war). Therefore, most of the information set forth in the attached sheets is to be taken as provisional and subject to revision.

BY COMMAND OF LIEUTENANT GENERAL DOOLITTLE

MEEDLE W. HOBBS
Major   AGD
Asst Adj Gen

The PRU coverage referred to in the General Doolittle letter was photo reconnaissance pictures taken of the Peenemunde site, which then was being surveyed by the Allies for its role in the development of the so-called revolutionary "secret weapons," of which Hitler had spoken so often. The first photographs showed

The formidable ME-262 German fighter, in concert with the ME-163, presented a real challenge to Allied fighter pilots who were charged with the defense of the bomber forces. One version of the ME-262 utilized jet-rocket engines in combination in order to boost its performance.

two of the mysterious ME-163's on the parking apron of the air strip there. Another showed a similar fighter positioned beside a tow truck. As a result of the piecing together of this intelligence crossword puzzle, plus the fact that there might be some substance to the claim of the Germans that they did indeed have some wonder weapons in the process of development, high priorities were given to the gathering of extensive information about the strange airplane and its potential use in combat against the Allied bombers, which were wreaking havoc on the German war machine.

The apprehension as to the employment of these potent new fighters was well founded, for in the summer of 1944, first reports of engagements with this revolutionary series of aircraft were made by American bomber and fighter crews over the European continent.

On July 28, 1944, a P-51 pilot met two of the little barrel-shaped bolts of lightning in flight, and he described the action in an official debriefing report:

I encountered the two ME-163 fighters over Merseburg at 0946 on 28 July 1944. My eight ship section was furnishing close escort to a combat wing of B-17's that had just finished bombing Merseburg. The bombers were heading south at 24,000 feet and we were flying parallel to them at about 1,000 yards to the east at 25,000 feet. Someone called in contrails at six o'clock. I looked back and saw two contrails at about

32,000 feet, about five miles away. I immediately called them to flight as jet propelled A/C (aircraft). There is no mistaking their contrails. The contrail was white and very dense, as dense as a cumulous cloud, and about the same appearance, except that it was elongated. The two contrails I saw were about three-fourths of a mile long.

We immediately dropped tanks and I turned on gun switches while making a 180-degree turnback toward the bandits. It has since turned out in interrogations that there were five ME-163's in a flight of two, which I saw with jets on, and another flight of three without jets. The two I saw made a diving turn to the left, in good, close formation, and started a six o'clock pass at the bombers. As soon as they turned, they cut off their jets. We started a head-on overhead pass at them, getting between them and the rear of the bombers. When they were still about 3,000 yards from the bombers, they saw us and made a slight turn to the left into us, away from the bombers. Their bank was about 80 degrees in this turn, but they only changed course about 20 degrees. They did not attack the bombers. Their rate of roll appeared to be excellent, but radius of turn very large. I estimate conservatively that they were doing between 500 and 600 miles per hour. Although I had seen them start their dive and watched them throughout the attack, I had no time to get my sights anywhere near them. Both ships, still in close formation and without jet propulsion, passed about 1,000 feet under us. I split-essed [a maneuver for losing altitude rapidly] to try to follow them. As soon as they passed under us, one of them continued on in a 45-degree dive and the other pulled up into the sun, which was about 50 to 60 degrees above the horizon. I glanced quickly up into the sun but could not see this one. When I looked back at the one that had continued to dive, approximately a second later, he was about five miles away down to perhaps 10,000 feet. Although I did not see it, the leader of my second flight reports that the a/c that pulled up into the sun used his jet in short bursts. The flight leader described it as looking like he was blowing smoke rings. This ship disappeared and we don't know where he went. The airplane is a beautiful thing in the air. It was camouflaged a rusty brown, similar to some of the FW-190's, and was highly polished. It looked as though it had been waxed. The published drawing of the aircraft is very accurate. Though these two pilots appeared very experienced, they were not aggressive and apparently were just up for a trial spin.

To lend credence to the report by the P-51 pilot, six B-17 crews also told of encountering two of the same ME-163's described by him.

The following day a P-38 flight encountered another of these unusual little intruders. The official report went on to furnish additional details:

An ME-163 was engaged at 1145 hours at 11,000 feet over Weser-münde by a flight of P-38's, which were escorting a B-17 straggler. The ME-163 made a slight low pass from five o'clock at the B-17, following through with a slight dive and then leveling off. Two P-38's pursued the E/A [enemy aircraft], which made a second slight dive and then climbed, weaving all the time. During the weaving, one P-38 closed in and opened fire, observing hits. The ME-163 climbed to 16,000 feet with intermittent bursts of smoke. It is not known whether the smoke was from the propulsion unit, or strikes. At 15,000 feet the ME-163 circled to the left and the P-38 turned inside, getting in a good deflection shot. Closest range estimated to be 300 yards. The E/A did a mild split "S" and spiraled off into an 80-degree dive, still giving out smoke.

The P-38 followed in a 70 to 80-degree dive, firing and observing strikes until the E/A pulled away. The P-38 pulled out of its dive at 4,000 feet. The ME-163 went into the overcast at 3,000 feet in a 90-degree dive at 500 miles per hour, plus. The P-38 dove again and pulled out at 1,500 feet, below the undercast, but the ME-163 could not be seen. The engagement lasted from three to four minutes.

The operations reports began to mount. Although there was never a moment of panic because these new aircraft made an appearance in the skies, there was considerable thought and conversation about them, with speculation as to what the Allies' opposition might be if they continued to increase in numbers.

What was this strange new menace in the skies over Germany? The propulsion groundwork for this airplane was actually laid in the first tests flights of the HE-112 and the HE-176, although the aircraft themselves bore no resemblance at all to each other.

The design of the ME-163 was a radical departure from those of all the so-called conventional fighter aircraft of the day. Unlike the HE-176, the ME-163 had no horizontal tail surfaces and its wings were swept back at a rather sharp angle. Its fuselage was anything but sleek and streamlined in appearance. However, its barrel shape was deliberately planned that way for a very practical reason, and was not just a flaw in the design. The bulging body was necessary to accommodate the rocket power plant.

The initial aeronautical experimenting which led up to the construction of the ME-163 was done in the mid-thirties by a brilliant young aircraft designer named Alexander Lippisch. His earliest work explored various techniques which would result in a more efficient type of glider. He was very active with his glider studies in the Rohn Mountains where Eric Stamer flew his gliders with solid rocket motors. Lippisch was convinced that to build by conventional methods the wings of an aircraft destined to fly at speeds to which rocket power was capable of propelling it would never realize the real potential of this newly discovered power source. He was determined to prove the merit of the swept-wing design which is now considered so indispensable in the construction of modern aircraft.

The efforts of Professor Lippisch were certainly paradoxical, to say the least, when one considers that he intended to blend the flight characteristics of a powerless glider with the very efficient propulsive potential of the rocket engine. Yet, he did exactly this, and history vividly records how well.

Through the 1930's, Lippisch continued to work at glider research and his efforts had their ups and downs. Several of his projects resulted in crashes involving some of Germany's most renowned fliers. These tragic events, coupled with the uncertain political atmosphere in Germany, were not exactly conducive to orderly research. However, this dauntless experimenter finally gained the confidence of the Air Ministry to the degree that they permitted him to start construction of a special aircraft called Project X. The title was indicative of the extremely secret nature of the program. All activity connected with it took place in a specially planned room and only people directly associated with the aircraft were permitted access to the premises.

One aspect of the project that was a surprise, even to Lippisch, was that it was to be powered by a special liquid rocket power plant. At this point, the project began to parallel the efforts of the Heinkel research. However, Lippisch was very pessimistic about the outcome. He felt that aside from its very basic research potential, the Heinkel-176—which was destined to become the first pure rocket aircraft in the world to fly—would never lead to any practical end.

Considerable strides were made on Project X in the ensuing months, but Lippisch was becoming very disenchanted with the political scheme of things and the constant security harassment surrounding him in the conduct of his research. For these reasons he decided to leave the German Research Institute for Sailplanes, and join the Messerschmitt firm in Augsburg. He took with him twelve assistants who represented some of the best aeronautical research talent in all Germany. Among them was Heini Dittmar, one of Germany's greatest test pilots.

Shortly after this move, a special section was formed within the Messerschmitt plant for the development of a high-performance rocket interceptor. The work of Lippisch and his group now came under the auspices of the Aeronautical Aircraft Development Department of the Luftwaffe.

The period was now 1938 and peace hung in the balance and war seemed imminent as the thirteen researchers settled down to work —and work they did—a fact which history in a few short months would indelibly record. Because of the war tensions in Europe, the project was given a rather low priority in deference to more conventional and proven aircraft, such as the famous ME-109 and the FW-190.

The rocket interceptor to which the group now turned their attention grew out of one of the earliest projects at the Research Institute for Sailplanes. This was given the designation of DFS-194. Lippisch did not stay at the Institute long enough to see that particular program through. In his new capacity at Messerschmitt, however, the transposed group took up where they left off at the Institute, and got down to the task of modifying a new glider, which was well along in construction, to accommodate a rocket engine. As a power plant they selected a Walter motor which would develop a total thrust of 1,650 pounds. In early 1940, after months of diligent effort, the craft was completed and the project was transferred to Peenemunde, on the northern coast of Germany, in order to conduct the flight trials.

Although they expected nothing spectacular in the way of high speed or maneuverability, Heini Dittmar managed to pilot the little glider plane to speeds in excess of 341 miles per hour. The results were considered adequate in terms of research data, and the flight did increase interest in the rocket interceptor program, a program which had been plagued by low-priority restrictions for many months.

Finally, an approval was given for the construction of two proto-types which had been designated ME-163, a designation which lay dormant for many months as a mere number on paper. The first glider plane was completed in the winter of 1940 and the second in the early spring of 1941. Heini Dittmar made many towed flights in the aircraft and they proved highly successful. The gliding ratio was unbelievably impressive—twenty to one—which to the layman means that for every twenty feet of horizontal distance covered, one would lose only one foot of altitude. The aircraft had such insignificant drag characteristics that unusual speeds were reached

The earliest version of the ME-163 was the A model shown below. First flight tests were conducted in this aircraft. It was later used for the training of Luft-waffe combat pilots. The earliest training flights were unpowered. The pilot was towed to altitude and released. He would then glide back to his home base, landing dead stick on return.

without any power at all. The speed was attained, of course, by diving the craft and then making horizontal passes across the fields. This was done quite frequently as a means of instilling enthusiasm in the program among members of the Air Ministry and the Luftwaffe.

One person of considerable influence was duly impressed during one of Heini Dittmar's test flights. General Ernst Udet happened to be visiting the field near Augsberg, where the pilot was in the midst of test flying one of the prototypes. The general was accompanied by Alexander Lippisch, and as they drove among the hangars of the airfield, Udet spotted the tiny glider and asked Lippisch what it was. The latter replied that it was the ME-163. Before he could continue, Dittmar decided to dive toward the field and make a low pass near the hangars, at a speed in excess of 400 miles per hour. The fact that the aircraft made no noise other than the eerie sound of air whistling across its smooth lines caused Udet to inquire as to the type of power plant it used.

"None," replied Lippisch.

"Impossible," replied Udet.

As the two continued to joust verbally, Dittmar made several more passes across the field to spend the energy he had generated by the almost vertical dive earthward a few moments prior. After a final pass across the vantage point of the viewers, whom he had spotted, he came in for a near-perfect landing. As Dittmar scrambled out of the stubby craft, Udet and Lippisch raced over to the area where he had stopped. Upon examining the plane closely, Udet remarked, "It's true. There is no engine."

The flight of this day had been a real stroke of good fortune for the rocket interceptor because Udet was genuinely impressed and he promised his wholehearted support in obtaining a higher priority for its development. This was a complete reversal of Udet's previous point of view for he had scoffed at the Heinkel-Warsitz efforts in flying the HE-176. This inconsistent personality trait was obviously more significant than was realized at the time, for a few months later the general committed suicide. Most people who knew him well attributed his actions to the unbearable pressures which

Hitler and his hierarchy were bringing to bear on the Luftwaffe. The powered flights with the ME-163 began in the summer of 1941 and Dittmar, with little effort, knocked off all existing world speed records. However, no one at the time publicly acknowledged this, for the flights were held in the strictest of secrecy. After attaining what he considered to be the maximum speed possible, within the limitations of his fuel supply, Dittmar decided to put on a full load of the highly volatile fuel and instead of taking off under rocket power, he would have a tow plane pull him aloft to an altitude best suited for an all-out speed run.

On October 2, 1941, he was towed to an altitude of 13,000 feet, where he cast off the towing cable and fired the rocket engine. The ME-163 darted ahead with unbelievable speed. As the instruments reached 683.85 miles per hour, the craft went out of control and careened violently around the sky. Sensing the probable end for him if he did not rectify things quickly, Dittmar cut the rocket engine. Seconds later, he regained control, but what this intrepid test pilot had experienced would prove to be the next great hurdle to overcome in aviation. Heini Dittmar had knocked at the door of the sound barrier. He had entered a flight condition which, in those days, aviators called compressibility.

The officials of the Air Ministry were skeptical that speeds such as those reported to have been attained by Dittmar were possible, and it took a critique by several highly regarded aeronautical experts to convince them that the event was factual. On the other hand, General Udet was exuberant over the results of the flight and he immediately began to press for the fitting of armament to the ME-163. He also recommended immediate large-scale production.

Lippisch, although elated at the general's reactions, managed to persuade him that much more testing was in order and that test facilities and personnel would have to be expanded to handle such a project before it would be safe to turn over the airplane to operational squadrons.

With overwhelming pressures being brought to bear to get the Komet—as it was now designated—ready for combat duty, a test group was organized, called Test Commando 16. During the ensu-

The three views of the ME-163 Komet shown above indicate the menacing appearance of the little barrel-shaped fighter. The wheels attached to the bottom were dropped after the aircraft broke ground. Upon return for landing, the skid, shown just above and between the wheels in a retracted position, was lowered.

ing months, these valiant pilots were engaged in shaking down the cantankerous little bird for a grueling combat role in the sky. It was a saga of great courage. Bad luck plagued the program constantly, in a contest which pitted man against a lethal and unforgiving machine, unforgiving in the sense that one mistake could mean instant death. Thirty test pilots were assigned to the project, and of that number only one-third survived. To fly this fickle little bundle of lightning was a constant gamble with fate.

The most precarious aspect of the Komet's character was the type of fuel used in its propulsion systems, which, like the HE-176, were also hypergolic. There were two rocket engines used in the ME-163 program. One was referred to as the cold-type unit. This utilized T-stoff (80 per cent hydrogen peroxide, plus oxyquinoline or phosphate as a stabilizer) and Z-stoff (an aqueous solution of calcium permanganate). The other system, called the hot-type unit, utilized a variation of these mixtures, plus others, and gave off a very prominent flame as it spewed from the rocket nozzle.

The handling of the fuels for either unit was extremely risky, for the ingredients not only would ignite on contact with one another, but some of them would also ignite on contact with anything of an organic nature. Things as minute as an insect or a dust particle could ignite great storage tanks—with catalysmic consequences! A mechanic for the test unit accidently demonstrated this with great violence when he poured a bucket of one fuel substance into a container which held the other reactant. He did not live long enough to know what happened. Special smocks had to be worn by the ground crewmen who handled the fueling of the Komets and the highly volatile liquids could only be kept in containers which were compatible with their chemical composition.

The greatest possible risk that could befall a pilot was an assignment to a Komet unit, for this fighter was probably the most unorthodox aircraft in the entire world. It took off on wheels but as soon as it was in the air these were dropped. This resulted in a more streamlined configuration and also made the aircraft lighter. In addition, construction was very simple and the on-board mechanisms were kept to a minimum, especially those which are normally actuated hydraulically.

The combat version of the Komet rocket fighter. Note the cannons mounted in the wing roots. The small propeller in the nose drove a generator which furnished electrical power for various systems within the aircraft.

Several pilots were lost on takeoff when the wheels, after being jettisoned, bounced back up, colliding with the aircraft and causing the rocket planes and their pilots to be consumed in giant fireballs.

Another characteristic of this volatile airplane was the manner in which the pilots had to land it. A small skilike skid, which was tucked up into the fuselage for takeoff, was lowered about seven inches below the fuselage for landing. This appendage was intended to absorb the shock of landing, which, on occasion, was rather severe. Severe pilots broke their backs and other more fortunate ones escaped with only ruptured or displaced vertebrae. The violence of the landings, coupled with the precariousness of the fuel on board, naturally did not make for a wholesome combination. On many missions, as the touchy aircraft skidded in across a bumpy dirt field at speeds of anywhere from 80 to 130 miles per hour, the fuel lines would rupture, permitting the fuels to get together, and an awesome sight would unfold! Most occurrences such as this ended in violent explosions, and the man in the machine stood little chance of survival.

Many pilots chose to jump from these potential fire bombs as the ominous clouds of fuel seeped into the cockpits upon touchdown. A remarkable number survived, however, although they sustained broken bones, broken necks, and broken backs. Still they considered this to be desirable in contrast to the awful fate which awaited a pilot who remained with an aircraft on the brink of explosion.

Although the price was extremely high, the performance of the sturdy little fighter improved as the months of test flying accumulated an abundance of new knowledge.

Many ranking officials of the Luftwaffe and the political hierarchy questioned the wisdom of building an operational rocket fighter. However, the desperate situation in which Germany now found herself, especially in the air war which was being waged in her skies, forced a quick decision to commit the ME-163 to combat.

The Komet was equipped with two thirty-millimeter cannons which were mounted in the wing roots. There were also plans (which went as far as the demonstration phase) to utilize rocket launching tubes in vertical mounts on the wings. With these the German planes could theoretically attack enemy bomber formations by flying underneath and firing the rockets upward. The mechanism for this firing was to be triggered by a light-sensitive cell, functioning like an automatic door which opens when someone steps in front of it. To prove this device, the Komets made passes at targets simulating enemy bombers. These consisted of strips of

Readying one of the ME-163's for takeoff was always an impressive sight to behold. Those involved in the program were very much aware of the precarious nature of the little beast, for they had seen the ill-fated demise of many a pilot.

The capability of the Komet is driven home in the photo above, as the rocket-powered fighter climbs after sending a B-17 down in flames over Germany. Two of the bomber's crew can be seen parachuting from the disabled craft while it plummets earthward.

cloth placed between two barrage balloons. The project did not reach extensive proportions and was never really developed for practical use.

As the end drew near for the Third Reich, everything, in the last desperate hours, was thrown into the melee. The test-pilot survivors of the original Commando 16 group were now given instructor roles in an effort to train a sufficient number of young pilots to man the entire ME-163 force currently available, which amounted to about 300 aircraft.

The first group of volunteers for Komet fighter units was made up of very youthful pilots who had just come from training in one of Germany's foremost gliding schools. Glider training was very desirable as a preliminary to ME-163 instruction, for every flight ended powerless, with a glide back to the base from which the airplane came. Out of the original twenty-eight cadets reporting, only seven elected to remain for the training after listening to the briefings on this unorthodox craft. Volunteers did sign up in considerable numbers, however, not only for the Komet squadrons, but also for other special fighter units which were being organized in an attempt to wrest control of the air back from the Allies. The plan called for the strategic positioning of high-performance fighters.

These now included the ME-262 jet, which had also entered the fighting in the vicinity of targets which were considered to have the highest priority by the Allied bombers, a force which was now pounding Germany around the clock and almost at will. The most desirable targets were the synthetic oil refineries. The Allied think-

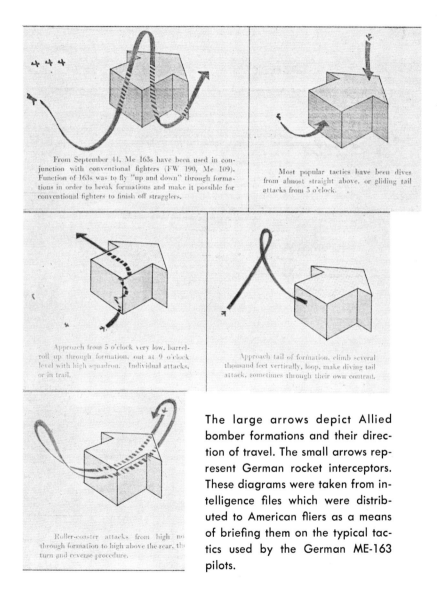

From September 44, Me 163s have been used in conjunction with conventional fighters (FW 190, Me 109). Function of 163s was to fly "up and down" through formations in order to break formations and make it possible for conventional fighters to finish off stragglers.

Most popular tactics have been dives from almost straight above, or gliding tail attacks from 5 o'clock.

Approach from 5 o'clock very low, barrel-roll up through formation, out at 9 o'clock level with high squadron. Individual attacks, or in trail.

Approach tail of formation, climb several thousand feet vertically, loop, make diving tail attack, sometimes through their own contrail.

Roller-coaster attacks from high no through formation to high above the rear, the turn and reverse procedure.

The large arrows depict Allied bomber formations and their direction of travel. The small arrows represent German rocket interceptors. These diagrams were taken from intelligence files which were distributed to American fliers as a means of briefing them on the typical tactics used by the German ME-163 pilots.

Once the initial shock of encounter with such a revolutionary fighter was overcome, American fighter pilots perfected a tactic of waiting until the ME-163 had spent its fuel supply. When this became obvious, they would pounce on the prey. Without the benefit of power, little maneuvering was possible, except the energy obtained through diving from high altitudes. Another tactic called for a certain number of American fighters to position themselves near the known Komet airfields. As the Komet pilots returned for landing, they were sitting ducks for the kill, as shown in the gun camera photos here.

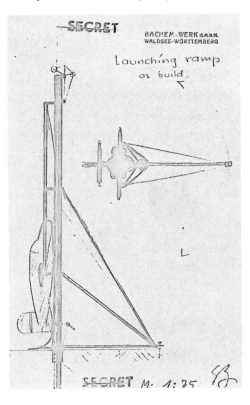

One of the earliest drawings of the Natter, obtained by agents, confirming the desperate measures to which the Germans were resorting in an effort to counter the effects of the Allied bombings.

lutionary machine which could be produced in an absolute minimum amount of time and with the barest of training for its pilots and ground crewmen.

With these guidelines in mind, a special Luftwaffe group conceived a plan which they chose to call the Natter (Viper) project. It called for the quick development of an aircraft which required no airfield from which to take off or land. In fact, once launched, the plane would never land intact—for such was the weird nature of the plane. The scheme called for an extremely small airplane, to be made of the most readily available materials which, at this time, seemed to be wood and crude steel. The next requirement was simplicity of manufacture, so simple, in fact, that the planners wanted to press all cabinetmakers, furniture companies, and small metal shops into the construction program. Thousands of small manufacturers would mass produce the Natter in such huge quantites that, assuming a very low success in kill rate against the Allied force, by sheer numerical superiority the enemy bombers could be wiped from the skies.

The basic design called for a very small interceptor, just a little more than twenty feet in length, with a wing span of around twelve feet, to be built for interception of bombers. The mission was not to be suicidal, although things were so desperate at this point that some scattered efforts had been made to organize several suicide units for ramming American and British aircraft. The stubby interceptor was to be launched vertically up a tower, which would stand some fifty feet in height. The tower, when lowered, could also serve as a trailer for two Natters, to be used in transporting them from place to place whenever air attacks required that they be moved to new locations, nearer the regions where aerial encounters were most likely to occur. Upon launching, extremely high G-forces, acting on the pilot, would make it difficult for him to look around to spot the enemy bomber formations. For this reason, the craft was to be linked to an antiaircraft gun radar as a means of steering it automatically to-

A Natter newly transported to the launch site for final assembly. Note the material from which it was constructed and the rather crude finish of its exterior. The device resting on the trailer in the foreground is one of four launch rockets used to propel the craft up the launch tower.

ward the general vicinity of the oncoming formations. When the pilot, after shaking off the G-induced forces, was able to spot the Allied aircraft visually, he could take over manually and direct the aircraft toward the approaching bombers. He would then take deadly aim and launch a salvo of twenty-four rockets at the formation, hoping they would take their toll. His chore complete, he would then make a violent turn away from the formation and dive steeply, in order to evade the lethal barrage of lead that the bombers' gunners would no doubt lay down.

Safely beyond the range of the bombers' guns, the Natter pilot would watch his air-speed indicator in order to determine when he could bail out of the aircraft safely. A special innovation was designed to accomplish this. When the pilot decided he could bail out safely, he would push a button which would separate the nose section from the other part of the fuselage. Simultaneously with this move, a parachute would deploy from the rear of the aircraft. The force of the parachute's opening shock would pull the rear of the fuselage completely away from the nose section. With this maneuver successfully completed, the pilot would slide out of his seat and, after a momentary delay to assure safe separation, open his personal parachute. If all the systems were working as planned, a timer, which was set in motion with the first sequence of events, would eject from the fuselage the rocket engine which was attached to a rear parachute, permitting it to float safely to the ground for reuse. The other parts of the aircraft would plunge on earthward to certain destruction. These maneuvers represented the basic philosophy of the Natter plan—salvage only the two most valuable ingredients on board, the rocket engine and the pilot.

Unlike the ME-163 pilot training program, which required that a young man have a basic course in glider training, there were no formal requirements for the potential Natter pilot other than the desire to participate in an unbelievably bold program. As a matter of fact, most of his training would be conducted in the classroom and his first flight would most likely be an actual attack on an enemy bomber formation. The reason for not including a significant flying training in the project was in keeping with the need of the Germans to save time. The most difficult and time-consuming thing to teach a fledgling pilot is the technique of landing. Therefore, complete flight training, including solo, was ruled out.

As with the ME-163 program, the Natter accent was on youth, for young men could withstand the rigors of high altitude and extreme gravity forces better than older men. Admittedly, older men would have been more difficult to recruit as volunteers, because of the fantastic nature of the mission, especially the more experienced pilots, for this was an unconventional way to run an air force, to say the least!

Some thought was given to the attaching of a Natter cockpit to the nose section of a twin-engine fighter and so give the future Natter pilot an opportunity to make runs on other training airplanes which would simulate his attack on an enemy bomber formation. In this way he would get the feel of the airplane controls. Another scheme called for the projection of aircraft silhouettes on a screen at which he would direct a mechanically-driven replica of the Natter for aiming practice.

The Natter would utilize the same rocket engine which had been developed and used in the ME-163 interceptor.

The Natter pilot would not be plagued with one of the dilemmas which the ME-163 pilot faced so frequently, namely, the dangerous landing on skids with fuel remaining on board, for he would never participate in any landing at all. In addition to the liquid Walter engine, a combination of solid rockets, which could vary from two to four, depending on the position of the enemy aircraft, or how rapidly he wanted to make the interception, would hurl the little black craft aloft. The solids would be utilized for the takeoff phase of the flight and dropped shortly after clearance of the tower, leaving the liquid unit alone to handle the job of propelling the tiny wood-and-steel monster on toward the bombers. The liquid engine would burn until the fuel had been expended. Even though the Natter could sustain propulsive thrust for only about eight seconds, this was sufficient to propel the fighter vertically as fast as the top speed of any of the fighters, which would be escorting the bombers. This was a great tactical advantage, for the interceptor could emerge from directly underneath the bombers and be within firing range before the fighters were even aware of its presence, so they could not get in position to defend their charges. Its rate of climb was around 475 miles per hour. This was about the top speed of the P-51 in level flight, which was the most frequently used fighter escort for Allied bombers over Germany. Horizontal speed was on the order of 730 miles per hour. In addition to this phenomenal vertical speed, the M-23 also possessed exceptional altitude characteristics—in excess of 32,000 feet. The bombers, for the most part, operated between 25,000 and 32,000 feet, so their altitude range was completely blanketed.

Production of the Natter aircraft began in September 1944 and contracts went out to every conceivable small-shop craftsman to tool up to build various parts, whatever his specialty might be.

The first Natters were completed and delivered for testing in October 1944. Officials in charge of the program were very optimistic that, within a very few months thereafter, they could boost production to between 5,000 and 10,000 of these perky little weapons per month.

In spite of the pressures for getting it into service, a very careful sequence of testing was planned for the aircraft in the Natter program, if not for the pilots. The first test called for the airplane to be towed aloft, in order to determine its flight characteristics. It was mounted beneath a Heinkel-111 bomber by means of an extendable boom.

Upon reaching an appropriate altitude for the tests, the pilot, who had ridden in the smaller aircraft ever since it left the ground, was able to maneuver it around by means of a swiveling socket mount. During these first tests, the little craft showed signs of having insufficient lift characteristics, probably because of the position at which the boom had been attached, rather than the inherent flight characteristics of the manned missile itself.

Upon release from the mother plane, it became so unstable that the pilot had to abandon it. The craft was completely demolished on impact with the ground. The next four trial flights involved the testing of the parachute recovery system, not only for the pilot but

The Natter being readied for one of its test flights. The tower from which it was launched was also intended to serve as a trailer. This permitted the craft to be moved to various places, depending on where the greatest defensive needs existed.

for the vehicle itself as well. All of these efforts were failures and, in every case, the aircraft was lost.

The sixth in the test series called for another manned flight of the missile aircraft, towed this time behind a Heinkel-111. However, a major modification had been made in the M-23's configuration. This time a tricycle landing gear had been attached, in order to retrieve the rocket plane through a conventional landing, rather than have it plunge back to earth to a fiery end. Although the landing gear had a distinct effect on its flying characteristics, the test went off well. The pilot, Zacher of the Balcham aircraft firm, piloted the missile, which flew very well and landed safely. Zacher was scheduled for further flights, which were designed to gather a variety of other data.

On December 18, 1944, the first launching of the Natter was attempted. The liquid rocket engine had not been installed up to this point. Four solid takeoff-assist rockets were attached to serve as the sole power plant. The near-vertical shot was of short duration, for the missile failed to develop sufficient thrust even to get all the way up the tower. It stuck halfway up the track which was enshrouded in electrical lines, and was completely consumed by fire, with the remains falling slowly back to the foot of the launching complex. The next tower flight was slightly more successful, for at least the missile cleared the top, but it immediately went into a bomblike trajectory, and met an untimely end, as had its predecessor.

Further attempts were made through the end of December 1944, and still met with only marginal results. This discouraging trend carried on into February. However, improvements were beginning to show by late February, which was rather remarkable in the light of the rapid pace at which the preparation had been made for the various tests. But near February's end, high-ranking officers of the SS had become impatient and demanded that the program be accelerated even further. They ordered that a manned takeoff with the liquid rocket engine and four solid rockets be accomplished at once. The planned test cycle was still far from complete at this point, but the officials in charge of the program were placed under such unusual coercion that they had no alternative but to make the attempt.

The half missile, half airplane was made ready on the first day of March 1945. Flight Lieutenant Sieber of the Luftwaffe volunteered as the pilot for the test flight. Lieutenant Sieber, a former ME-163 pilot, was very eager to make the first manned flight in this weird hybrid. One of the bleak ironies surrounding the venture was the fact that, at the moment of launching, thousands of American bombers had infested the skies over Germany. They passed within scant miles of the site of origin of the Natter aircraft which, in the minds of the people who worked there, was the one defensive system destined to seal their doom.

The skies were overcast as Sieber was strapped into the squatty beast. He checked the flight controls, fitted his oxygen mask, and took note of the scant number of instruments at which he had to look. These were located, from his perspective, in the cockpit's ceiling, for he was strapped in a lying-on-his-back position, facing straight up. A window had been cut in the floor of the Natter,

Flight Lieutenant Sieber, a Luftwaffe test pilot, is launched up the tower on the first manned test of the Natter. Seconds after this photograph was taken, the canopy came off, knocking Sieber unconscious. The craft then went into an uncontrolled loop, then onto its back, plunging the pilot and the Natter to inevitable destruction.

through which the pilot could watch the horizon as he shot upward. On operational missions this was also intended to permit him visual references, as to where the bombers would be in relation to his own position. For a former fighter pilot this was a most unorthodox position in which he now found himself.

The canopy was closed and Sieber was enshrouded in the eerie monster. The ground crew began to count down the launching as Sieber lay poised for the high-gravity forces which would soon press him into his seat as the rockets propelled him like a straw on the wind up the girder-like structure at vertical speeds never before experienced by a human being. He alone was charged with igniting the rockets, which would blast him upward. Hesitating for only a moment after completing his check list, Sieber pushed the button and the rockets sprang alive, engulfing the tower in a sheet of flame. The awkward-looking craft bolted from the tower under full thrust of the liquid and the solid rockets, working in unison. At an altitude of around 300 feet, the Natter turned on its back in an erratic maneuver. The ground crewmen sensed that something had gone terribly wrong. The missile-plane continued to climb at an angle of about thirty degrees. During this unbelievably rapid climb, the plastic hood was seen falling from the fuselage. Then the liquid rocket engine suddenly went silent. The out-of-control craft now traveled on momentum alone, and it was only a matter of time until the sure hand of gravity took hold to return it earthward. Reaching an altitude of around 5,000 feet, and darting momentarily into a low-lying cloud, the craft turned sharply, heading for the earth and certain doom. Now in a near-vertical dive, the Natter plummeted downward, carrying Lieutenant Sieber to a fiery death, in full view of the men who had assisted in launching him only seconds before.

After—outwardly, at least—regaining their composure upon witnessing such a horrifying experience, the official near the launching site began to investigate the possible causes of the ill-fated flight.

The actual summary of their official findings reads as follows, translated from the German:

Preliminary Brief Test Report on M-23
First Vertical Launching of the Piloted Missile with Power
Plant Takeoff Assists, March 1, 1945

On March 1, 1945, pilot Sieber performed the first launching with a piloted missile from the Heuburg.

The missile was set for full thrust. Sieber ignited the takeoff assists and the missile left the mount satisfactorily. After attaining an altitude of approximately 100 meters, the missile made a sharp turn in an upside-down position. The missile continued to climb, being inclined about thirty degrees, whereby the hood dropped from the missile. After further climb to an altitude of approximately 1,500 meters, the power plant stopped approximately fifteen seconds after launching. Thereupon the missile went into a power dive and hit the ground practically in a vertical descent, landing a few kilometers from the place of takeoff, thirty-two seconds later. During the entire flight the pilot made no attempt to save himself.

The first vertical takeoff of a piloted missile revealed the following:

1. It is assumed—and is highly probable—that the missile turned so rapidly on its back because the pilot, dazed by the takeoff procedure, released the control stick arresting device, set forward two degrees, whereby he pulled up the missile involuntarily, because of the accelerating forces.

2. Upon termination of the upside-down curve, the missile climbed in inverted position at approximately thirty degrees. It might be assumed that the pilot's head was pushed against the hood by his own weight, so that the hood dropped off. While the hood lock had worked satisfactorily during a flight test with M-8 up to a velocity of 600 km per hour, it can nevertheless be stated that the lock was too weak to withstand the extraordinary stress. Hence the hood lock must be made stronger.

3. Since the hood and the attached head cushion fell off, the pilot struck his head against the back wall at high acceleration and probably became unconscious, so that he lost control over the missile temporarily. It is even possible that the pilot broke his neck at that moment, since his head was thrown back with such violence and since he slipped partly out of the missile, as far as the safety belt would permit.

4. Since during the entire flight the pilot made no attempt to save himself, it is to be assumed that during all this time he was completely dazed, or that he was not clear of his position in space after having shut

Frontal view of the Natter shows the lethal armament which it carried. This particular version was fitted for twenty-four high velocity rockets. Other versions were equipped with rapid fire machine guns—or a combination of both.

off the power plant, so that he pulled out toward the vertical instead of remaining horizontal. Conclusions to be drawn from the above findings:

The gravity load acting on the pilot and during takeoff and possibly resulting confusion concerning the pilot's position in space require, as emphasized before, that the takeoff process and the approximate target approach must be completely mechanized. Only the approach flight on enemy, i.e., firing approach (such as optical sighting of bombers), shall be left to the pilot.

It is our opinion that another takeoff with pilot is not to be made unless several missiles with automatics and without pilot have been flown satisfactorily. The first high-angle takeoff with automatics and without pilot is set for approximately March 10, 1945.

If, however, another high-angle start without automatics and with a pilot should be made, it could take place around March 5, upon completion of the second manned missile (M-25). Changes will consist in the heavier hood locking device and in locking the stick during takeoff in such a manner that the pilot cannot move the stick readily when suffering from shock, whereby a vertical ascent of the missile during the first 1,000 meters would be practically assured.

We suggest that the decision to this effect be reserved for the SS-RHA or OKL (the two research organizations charged with development responsibility), as we do not approve a repetition of this test because disclosures with respect to further developments do not seem to warrant it.

(END OF REPORT)
Waldsee, 2 March 1945

As happened with so many other programs which were designed to turn the tide of aerial warfare, programs such as the ME-262 jet fighter and the ME-163 rocket interceptor—again time ran out. No further manned tests were made and the few unmanned efforts were really all in vain, for the Natter missile airplanes would never have occasion to intercept American bombers, for Germany's collapse was now very imminent. This was a stroke of good fortune for the crews who manned the latter, because the Natter had great combat potential and, given time, it could have been developed into a very lethal air-defense system for use in the skies over Germany. Near the war's end, an even more formidable rocket fighter evolved from the ME-163 basic design. This was labeled the ME-263. The Allied air crews could be thankful that time was on their side and

In a frantic effort to drive off the hordes of Allied bombers, thoughts were given by the German High Command to suicide and ramming missions to destroy the attackers. In addition to the Natter, a piloted version of the famous V-1 buzz bomb was also considered. The one shown above was a part of the flight test program to develop such an aircraft.

that the Natter never had a chance to challenge seriously their supremacy of the air over the European continent.

History will never conspicuously record Flight Lieutenant Sieber's name among the aeronautical pioneers. However, he did contribute a notable first in astronautics. He was the first man, prior to Yuri Gagarin, to be launched vertically by rocket power alone. This event might very well be considered one of the many plateaus which ultimately led to man's present status in the conquest of space.

5

Bombing North America
from Space

At the close of World War II, a series of weapons were employed by the Germans. They referred to them as "wonder weapons," "secret weapons," and a host of other titles, intended primarily as propaganda efforts. These weapons were launched by the thousands, they were not extremely accurate or effective because of their small payload-carrying capability and lack of efficient guidance systems. They were nevertheless tremendous feats of propaganda because they dealt in the realm of the mysterious. The "wonder weapons" were the famous V-1 and V-2, or vengeance weapons, as Hitler chose to call them. Although they were the products of war, they formed the most substantial foundation for the exploration of outer space that the world had ever known. They became the basic tools with which man would someday break the bonds of earth's gravity and fly to the moon and the planets beyond.

The V-1 and the V-2 were more than sufficient to startle the world, and they did wreak a certain amount of damage during the bombings of London and Antwerp, nevertheless, they were rather incidental in the master scheme of planning among the scientific community in Germany. As far as the United States was concerned,

The V-2 missile startled the world when it was introduced as "the wonder weapon" of World War II.

these weapons, in the hands of the axis powers, posed no direct threat, for other than a few efforts by the Japanese to bomb the mainland by means of randomly released balloons, which were to be carried by the prevailing westerly winds, and an attempt or two to bombard the West Coast with submarines, this country had sustained no significant damage as a result of enemy action.

One of the most significant German research programs, in the greatest of secrecy, which could eventually have sent lethal payloads on their way to New York City—and other American cities— began to unfold during the year 1945.

The V-2—or the A-4, as it was more properly called—could hit targets at a range of about 200 miles. Areas within the British Isles, including London, or on the eastern coast of the European continent, offered the only worth-while targets covered by the maximum reach of this weapons system. Drastic changes would have to be made on the V-2, or an entirely new rocket developed, in order to take war via rocket to other, and more distant, Allied targets. Again facing the grim reality that time was running out for them, the undertaking of another missile development seemed completely out of the picture to the Germans. The only thing that could be done in the eyes of their German experts would be to modify the V-2 in some manner that would extend its range. After lengthy discussions among the military and civilian leaderships, a decision was made to add wings to the fuselage of the basic missile, the V-2, with no change in the propulsion system. In this way, aerodynamic lift would take effect, once the missile returned from the vacuum of space to regions of the sensible atmosphere, thus permitting the range to be extended by means of gliding. Flight tests later confirmed that by the use of wings, the range of the system could be doubled while retaining essentially the same control in order to hit more distant targets.

With the modification complete, the V-2 was given a new designation—the A-9. As knowledge and test experience grew, a new concept evolved for military deployment of the A-9. This included the addition of a "crew," consisting of a single pilot housed in a pressurized cabin. There would also be a retractable undercarriage, a manually operated steerable nose wheel, and special aerodynamic aids to landing, such as parachutes by which to slow the craft. However, the landing speeds were computed to be on the order of 100 miles per hour, which was considerably less than the landing speeds of the jet fighters then in service. A returning A-9 would be little more than a flying shell, for it would be completely empty of the fuel which would represent more than 90 per cent of its weight on takeoff. This would turn it into a very efficient glider upon returning from a mission.

In their search for ways of extending the range of the A-9 even further, the experimental group—headed by Wernher von Braun—gave considerable thought to the fact that a rocket that climbs to an altitude sufficient to take it into outer space simply means that it leaves the earth's atmosphere—or at least the sensible atmosphere—namely, an atmosphere sufficient to support a flyable vehicle. The initial phase of a rocket's climb out is the most taxing one in terms of fuel consumption, for the greatest drag is being exerted while it is moving through the densest region of the atmosphere. Fortunately, the air diminishes in density the higher the rocket climbs, which accounts significantly for the gradual acceleration of its speed. When it leaves the earth's atmosphere, its engine then becomes 100 per cent efficient, for there are no retarding forces other than those of gravity.

These considerations prompted the group to try to devise a means of saving the on-board fuel of the A-9 until it reached the outer fringes of the atmosphere, in order to obtain the maximum efficiency, hence the maximum range, from it. The scientists recalled the launching of the V-1's from an inclined ramp with an auxiliary booster, which led them to planning something similar for the A-9.

Experience had shown the A-9 engineers that a catapult with a very slight gradient could give the manned rocket an initial velocity of around 7,000 miles per hour—more than enough to send it well out of the atmosphere, where the on-board engine could be ignited. From then on it could attain unbelievable speeds for that era. The booster for use on the ramp was to consist of a cluster of two other V-2's—or possibly even four—which could be braked to a stop for reuse after spending themselves. These would be guided up the incline by massive lugs fitted around a rail, very similar to those used for a conventional railroad track.

A more advanced plan was considered later. This ruled out the need for elaborate launching facilities, such as the ramp just described. It called for the building of a mammoth rocket that could develop a thrust of more than 400,000 pounds. Keep in mind that these plans were formulated in 1945 and the present-day Titan II, which launched the Gemini astronauts, has a thrust of 430,000 pounds, an increase of only 30,000 pounds in a time interval of more than twenty years.

So elaborate were the advanced plans that this booster called for the inclusion of air brakes and special parachutes to be used to recover the vehicle after launching, for repeated use on other occasions.

All these calculations resulted in the proposed mating of the A-9 and the A-10, which was to give the Germans intercontinental range, meaning that the war could have been carried to North American shores. Incidentally, the first drawings of such a concept were made in 1941. An alternate plan for the construction of the

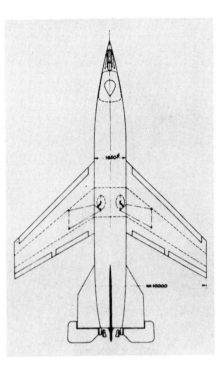

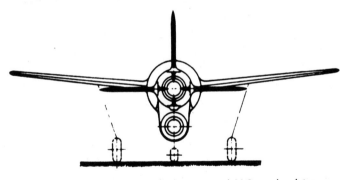

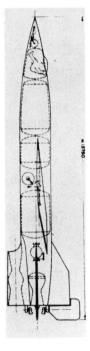

As World War II progressed, the original V-2 evolved into a more advanced and longer range winged version. The weapon was a prelude to a piloted weapon system which was ultimately destined to bomb North America.

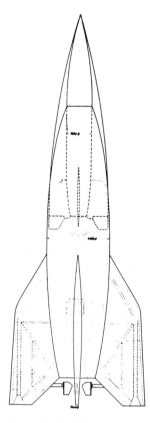

The A-10 booster shown here as it enshrouds
the smaller A-9, the latter being an advanced
version of the V-2. By mating the two systems,
the Germans contemplated bombing the North
American continent. These rockets were the
forerunners of both the American and Russian
space efforts.

A-10 included the use of a cluster of six engines, owing to the long
time which would have been required to develop a single-chamber
engine to perform this herculean task.

Three American cities were considered as targets in the calculations made by the German engineers, based on launching sites located in westernmost France, or in Portugal. The cities were Washington, New York, and Pittsburgh. The logic in hitting these cities
would have been mainly for psychological reasons rather than for
strategic value because the payloads carried would not have had
massive destructive power.

The piloted versions of the A-9 would have resulted in the first
space flight performed by earth-bound man, had they been carried
through to completion. The contemplated achievements of the A-9
could be compared to the suborbital flights of Commander Alan

Shepard and Captain Gus Grissom, except that the A-9 pilot would have traveled a much greater distance and would have flown the missile back and landed on an airfield, rather than making a descent by parachute into the ocean—again, if those early plans had materialized.

The targets considered for this first military space venture, which were all within range of the piloted A-9, were London, Dover, Liverpool, Birmingham, and Glasgow. Unlike the one-way trips to these targets of the V-2, or the unpiloted version of the A-9, the manned version could be flown back time and time again for reuse, as has just been indicated. The targets at the extreme limits of the A-9's range without the A-10 booster were considered only for the unmanned version. However, one extremely bold plan to strike at the westernmost cities of the British Isles called for the pilot to aim the missile at the city selected as a target and to eject in the vicinity of this target prior to the final plunge. After he had alighted in the water, or on land, the plan called for his pickup by a submarine which was assigned to loiter along the coast nearest to the target city, or for the pilot to escape overland, or spend the remainder of the war as a prisoner, if captured.

To sustain the range of the A-9, the pilot could actually bounce off the atmosphere like a stone skidding off a millpond, as a means of increasing the distances to be covered. Almost all calculations were based on attaining an initial height of more than 100 miles. The proposed flight plan for the bombing of the North American continent would have been an acknowledged propaganda feat; certainly far-reaching in its effect. However, unlike the round trip to "say London"—a relatively near target—the mission to New York or Washington or Pittsburgh would have had to be a one-way flight for the pilot. For this reason, two schools of thought prevailed on the subject.

The boldest plan contrived for the project envisioned the takeoff of the A-9, mated with the A-10, from a launching site on the coast of France, with an estimated flight time of around forty minutes, covering some 3,500 miles. Upon arrival over, say, New York City, the pilot would lock the controls of the A-9 in a trajectory which would send it plunging into the heart of the city.

Along the final trajectory, and at a prearranged geographic location the pilot would eject for eventual pick up by a submarine loitering off the coast. Alternate plans called for the pilot to drop a bomb load on the city and then bail out over land, permitting the missile to plunge at random to the countryside below. Or he could head the missile toward the city and bail out in its vicinity, where he would try to escape or await his fate and the outcome of the war as a prisoner.

Fortunately for the United States, such a fantastic program never materialized. The scope of the undertaking read like science fiction, but no one treated the scheme lightly, for there was positive proof of the practical talents, as well as the genius of this group of scientists. Many of these clever men had already introduced real-life versions resulting from some rather unbelievable imaginative technology—futuristic systems such as the V-2, the ME-163 Komet, the ME-262 jet fighter, and the Natter Viper. Anyone—and especially any German—would have been foolish to say that these things could not be done. A note of irony lies in the fact that the scientists most responsible for these farseeing concepts would soon join their former adversaries and form an elite nucleus of the inventors that has kept the United States out in front in the race for space.

Dr. Wernher von Braun, during one of the initial interrogations to which he responded just after his capture by American troops in 1945, commented on some of the more futuristic plans which he had helped to pioneer. His concluding remarks indicate just how far ahead the thoughts of his group extended.

In the more distant future, the development of liquid rockets offer, in our opinion, the following possibilities, some of which are of tremendous significance:

"(a) Development of long-range commercial planes and long-range bombers for ultra high speeds. The flight duration of a fast rocket aircraft going from Europe to America would be approximately forty minutes. It would even be possible to build very long-range bombers which would turn around at supersonic speeds in a very wide curve after having released their bombs, and return in a glide to land at their point of departure. The high speed of such aircraft would make defense against them ineffective with present-day means.

"(b) Construction of multistage piloted rockets, which would reach a maximum speed of over 7,500 meters per second outside the earth's atmosphere. At such speeds the rocket would not return to earth, as gravity and centrifugal forces would balance each other out. In such a case, the rocket would fly along a gravitational trajectory, without any power, around the earth, in the same way as the moon. According to the difference of the trajectory from the earth, the rocket could complete one circuit around the earth in any time between one and one-half hours and several days. The whole of the earth's surface could be continually observed from such a rocket. The crew could be equipped with very powerful telescopes and be able to observe even small objects, such as ships, icebergs, troop movements, construction work, etc. They could also carry out physical and astronomical research on problems which could only be tackled at that altitude and in the absence of the atmosphere. The importance of such an 'observation platform' in the scientific, economic, and military spheres is obvious. When the crew of the rocket want to return to earth all they need do is reduce the speed of the rocket slightly, which can be done by rocket propulsion. The rocket then enters the upper layers of the atmosphere tangentially and its speed is gradually reduced by friction. Finally, it can land like an ordinary airplane by means of wings and auxiliary gear. It would also be possible to relieve the crew and provision the 'observation platform,' by means of another rocket which could climb up to the platform and pull up beside it.

"(c) Instead of having a rocket set up as an 'observation platform' outside the earth, it would be possible later on to build a station especially for this purpose and send the components up into the interstellar space by means of rockets to be erected there. The erection should be easy as the components would have no weight in the state of free gravitation. The work would be done by men who would float in space wearing a diver's suit and who could move at will in space by means of small rocket-propulsion units, the nozzles of which they would point in the required direction.

"(d) According to a proposal by the German scientist, Professor Oberth, an 'observation station' of this type could be equipped with an enormous mirror, consisting of a huge net of steel wire onto which metal foils could be suspended. A mirror of this nature could have a diameter of many kilometers and its component facets could be controlled by the station which would enable the heat and light of the sun to be concentrated on selected points of the earth's surface. This would enable large towns, for instance, to get sunlight during the evening hours. The weather, too, can be influenced by systematic concentration of the sun's rays onto distant lakes and seas, and increasing their evaporation. The clouds thus formed could be driven to the required spot, influencing the centers of low and high pressure through radiation from other facets of the mirror. If the mirror is made large enough, and it could be of extremely light construction, it would even appear possible to generate deadly degrees of heat at certain spots of the earth's surface.

"(e) When the art of rockets is developed further, it will be possible to go to the other planets, first of all to the moon. The scientific importance of such trips is obvious. In this connection, we see possibilities in the combination of work done all over the world in connection with the harnessing of atomic energy, together with the development of rockets, the consequences of which cannot yet be fully predicted."

The futuristic vision of the whole Peenemunde group and the amazing accuracy with which they predicted the way space events would unfold tend to substantiate the fact that they were realistically sure of what they were planning and doing and not just idealistic dreamers.

Although the boldness of thought which pervaded the Peenemunde thinking was just about as advanced and incomprehensible to most people as any research could possibly be, there were, however, others who were just as eager to put the weapons of warfare into space. The most ardent advocate of harnessing the power of the rocket engine to winged craft, in order to send it into the yet-unexplored arena, was a professor from Stuttgart, Dr. Eugene Saenger. His concept would have been the first manned weapon to strike an adversary from the new and militarily unexploited dimension of space.

Dr. Eugene Saenger and Dr. Irene Brett (Mrs. Saenger), world-renowned mathematicians in professional life, had devoted most of their energies and thoughts during the thirties and the war years to theoretical astronautics and aeronautics.

About two years after Hitler assumed power in Germany, Dr. Saenger went to work for the Hermann Goering Institute, the research organization which conducted research and development for the Luftwaffe. He brought with him many years of experimenta-

Upon discovery of the "wonder weapons" being developed by the Germans, fleets of bombers were dispatched to Peenemunde, the development site for the weapons. Above photo shows some of the damage inflicted on the facility.

tion on rocket engines for fighter aircraft, with which he had obtained creditable results. Although no single project which ultimately took form as completed hardware bears his name, he will be forever remembered for instigating the most astounding weapons system conceived during World War II. As a matter of fact, Saenger had first given extensive thought to his program in the mid-thirties. As with so many other projects which were conducted under the veil of secrecy during that period, and certainly through the war years, it would be interesting to know how the rest of the world would have reacted had they been aware of some of the fantastic schemes which were being considered in Deutschland.

From a U. S. Army Air Forces survey, Von Braun's concept for creating a winged missile capable of bombing New York or Washington, it could be deduced that he would have sent the A-9 out of the atmosphere as a part of the flight plan, in order to gather the speed required to span those great distances between Germany and American cities. This period in space would have been very brief, occurring at the apogee (highest point) in the flight trajectory. During the remainder of the flight the craft would have skimmed the upper reaches or fringes of the earth's atmospheric blanket in a prolonged glide, but the venture could not have been considered as being a complete space mission in the truest sense.

By way of contrast, the plan of Dr. Saenger was so bold that it defied imagination. His scheme has been called by a variety of names, such as "Glide Bomber," "Boost Glide Bomber," "Skip Glide Bomber," and the "Antipodal Bomber." The latter title has gained the widest acceptance among those who have had occasion to become familiar with the program since the war's end. These people, in the main, have been the intelligence officers who interro-

Cutaway of the Antipodal Bomber, showing the pilot's compartment, the propellant tanks, and the rocket engine. The bomb load for the space bomber would have been on the order of ten tons.

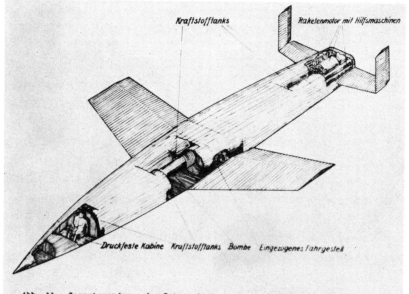

Kraftstofftanks   *Raketenmotor mit Hilfsmaschinen*

Druckfeste Kabine   *Kraftstofftanks*   *Bombe*   *Eingezwgenes Fahrgestell*

Abb. 33: Gesamtanordnung des Raketenbombers von 10 Tonnen Leergewicht.

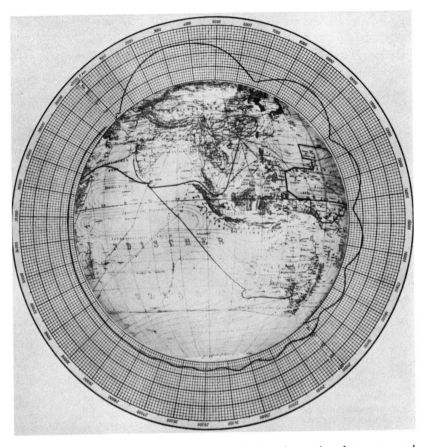

One of the global flight plans for the Antipodal Bomber, taken from captured German documents at the end of World War II. Note how the undulating skips diminish in altitude and distance, due to the loss of energy as the bomber makes contact with the atmosphere. At the end of the mission, the skips end and the return to the home base becomes a gradual glide.

gated the German scientists. The name "Antipodal Bomber" is derived from the world's antipodes which are simply points on the opposite sides of the world. It also divulges the intent of this fantastic machine. Saenger's plan called for the building of a 100-ton, piloted space bomber with which to blast cities of the North American continent. Being a very realistic scientist, he was well aware of the limitation of his space bomber, which was not quite capable of orbital flight because of lack of propulsive power. But, bolstered by the expert mathematical calculations of his wife, Dr. Brett, he was sure the Antipodal Bomber could make one revolution around the earth, even though not as a true orbital flight. However, the idea had occurred to him—and Dr Brett's calculations confirmed this—that if it was required of him, the pilot of the space bomber could make the trip all the way around the earth by skillfully manipulating the machine to perform undulating skips off the atmosphere. Each skip, owing to energy loss as a result of atmospheric friction, diminished in altitude and distance.

Theoretically, the mission would be flown in this fashion. The Antipodal Bomber would be hoisted on to a large cradle-like device positioned horizontally just in front of a massive booster, which was also horizontal to the ground. The units were suspended above the ground on three massive rails very similar to those used by railroads, but considerably more rugged. The upper rail supported most of the forces brought to bear by the bomber and booster, which came to a total weight of around 150 tons. The two other

Drawing shows the general arrangement for launching the Antipodal Bomber. The propulsive units behind the vehicle consist of V-2's strapped together forming essentially a single unit.

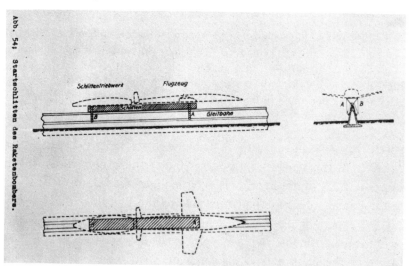

rails were attached near the bottom of the master concrete base supporting the launching track which, when viewed frontally, were positioned so as to form an isosceles triangle. The lower rails were intended only to absorb any possible side-to-side or rotational movements of the aircraft around its longitudinal axis. In either case, the highest-quality lubricants obtainable were to be utilized for the takeoff run because excessive friction would have meant a great loss in the final velocity of the aircraft at the end of the track. This would also have had a very critical bearing on the distance which the Antipodal Bomber could cover. Ideally, the propulsive unit behind the bomber could generate 1,200,000 pounds of thrust which, considered in today's frame of reference, is equivalent to the power required to launch almost four Gemini spacecraft into orbit. This would be a fantastic scheme at any time, but consider that it was worked out in the late thirties and the early forties.

Parallel to his studies in the creation of a winged rocket spacecraft, Dr. Saenger had also become very concerned about the ability of man to withstand the gravity forces associated with the employment of such massive power. His calculations showed that forces on the order of ten times those of normal gravity would be exerted on the space bomber's pilot for a period of several minutes.

Saenger had the benefit of many studies which had been conducted by Dr. Hubertus Strughold, a Luftwaffe flight surgeon who is recognized the world over as the father of space medicine. Strughold's research involved the drugging of primates and spinning them for periods of a minute or more, subjecting them to forces up to twenty times those of normal gravity. Strughold also acquired data on human subjects who had withstood forces up to seventeen G's for a period of up to three minutes. But no matter how reassuring the theoreticians were in the way of experimental data, it would not change the fact that the Antipodal Bomber pilot was sure to experience sensations unknown to that degree by any man on earth at that point in time.

The space bomber's launching track, about two miles in length, was to be laid out so that it was oriented west to east. This would give the aircraft-spacecraft the benefit of the rotation of the earth.

If we take an arbitrary line of latitude in mid-Germany, this would mean that the earth would impart a speed of around 800 miles per hour to the craft. To point it in any direction would nullify this advantage to an extent, depending on the degree of angular change.

After ignition of the large sled booster, the complete unit would move off, slowly at first, but the acceleration would mount rapidly. As the speed increased, the space vehicle would grow lighter with each foot per second increase in its forward velocity when the wings began to bite into the air which rushed past them. There would be no advantage on the part of the pilot to see how quickly he could take the aircraft off from the sled because the latter would serve as a source of brute power, and the longer the pilot could let the

The arrows thrusting from the drawing of the Antipodal Bomber indicate the magnitude and the directions of the forces exerted on the craft as it climbs toward its desired flight altitude for a given target. The arrow "G" indicates gravity; "P" the power of the rocket engine; "A" the lift factor determined by the shape and size of its wings; "T" the retarding forces of atmospheric friction. "C" represents the velocity and apparent direction of descent should the rocket power be stopped abruptly. The drawing at the right indicates the same forces at work from a different perspective.

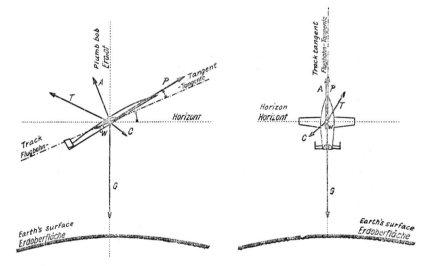

Abb. 59; Äussere Kräfte am Raketenbomber beim Anstieg.
External Forces to the Rocketbomber at the time of ascent

bomber linger there, the greater the velocity. Thus an increase in the craft's ability to make a trip around the world. According to Dr. Brett's computations, the hundred tons of fuel and metal should lift from the cradle after a two-mile run at a speed of around 1,000 miles per hour. The pilot would pull the craft up into a climb angle of about thirty degrees and would hold it in that attitude for about twenty-five seconds. During this period, he would also have important procedures to go through, such as selecting the proper course for putting the spacecraft over an intended target half a world away. This had to be done while the bomber was still in the atmosphere, for the maneuver would be prohibitively expensive in terms of fuel if it were performed in space and at this time Saenger had not contemplated reaction jets for space maneuvers. While flying in the atmosphere the action could be done aerodynamically with conventional airplane controls.

After the coasting period, which is not to say that the bomber would not still be climbing spaceward. On the contrary, the fantastic momentum acquired during powered flight would still be hurling the beast up through the outer fringes of the atmosphere. After a predetermined coasting interval, which had been carefully calculated, the pilot would ignite the rocket engine for the second part of his powered flight. This would burn until all of its fuel had been expended. By then, the bomber would have acquired sufficient energy, both potential (by virtue of altitude) and kinetic (by virtue of horizontal motion), to see its mission through to completion. Although the sled booster used to launch the Antipodal Bomber was conceptually as powerful as four of the Titan rockets which launched the Gemini astronauts into orbit, it would not have been capable of propelling the Antipodal Bomber into a celestial orbit, as we now know it. The reason, of course, was the fact that the bomber weighed approximately sixty-seven times more than a Gemini space craft.

Facing the reality that the bomber could not go into an elliptical or circular orbit, Saenger took the only other course available to him. He would have elected to fly the space bomber around the earth in a series of undulating skips, with each skip diminishing in

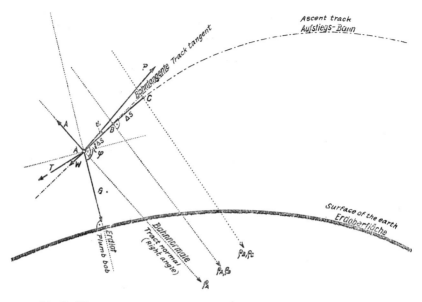

Abb. 60; Näherungsweise graphische Ermittlung der Aufstiegsbahn.
Approximate graphic determination of the ascent track

The above graph shows the mathematically predicted path which the Antipodal Bomber would have flown on its way to a target on the North American continent. A captured Luftwaffe document.

altitude and distance between successive skips.

Another very conspicuous reason for not desiring to fly in an elliptical or circular orbit was that the metal research of that day had not created alloys capable of withstanding the searing heat of re-entry. Saenger theorized that the pilot of the Antipodal Bomber could control the temperatures of his craft by regulating the length of time it was committed to atmospheric friction. The first skip which he would undertake on a global mission would be the most precarious maneuver, for the highest temperatures to be encountered would occur during this one. At that point in his mission, he would be traveling at peak velocity and the distance encompassed in the initial skip could span from 10 to 30 per cent of the circumference of the earth. The actual length of this skip would, of course, depend on the target selected and its specific location.

As I have said before, the bizarre space craft would sustain itself in flight by bouncing off the upper fringe of the earth's atmosphere like a stone bouncing over the smooth surface of a body of water. If one throws a stone across a smooth pond of water he will get an excellent idea of the physical laws which were brought into play in the Antipodal Bomber project. He will notice that the first skip is a long one and the bounces out of the water grow shorter and shorter, and lower and lower, as the stone loses its kinetic and potential energy. Finally, when all of the energy is spent, the stone plunges for the last time and sinks.

If this amateur researcher in space flight also experiments with stones having a variety of shapes, he will discover the distinct advantages that were designed into the Antipodal Bomber. If, for instance, he throws a stone with a flat bottom, it will skip with considerably greater ease and for a longer distance than one with a rough and misshapen lower side. It was for this reason that the lower part of the fuselage of the bomber was designed with very simple lines and a smooth flat finish.

Every skip by the Antipodal Bomber would mean the spending of critically needed energy. However, it simultaneously would serve the very practical purpose of slowing the airplane for a safe conventional atmospheric penetration—and landing—at the mission's end.

One of the most interesting aspects of the planning which went into this awe-inspiring weapon of space was the methodical way in which Dr. Saenger described its potential uses. To emphasize this point, a section of a "most secret" document which was seized from the Luftwaffe files by the Allies at the end of World War II is included—word for word—as written by Saenger.

VI. TYPES OF ATTACK

1. Basic Types of Attack

The type of attack procedure to be used by the rocket bomber in any specific case is determined by the nature of the target and its distance from the home base.

The extraordinary variety of targets is discussed in Section VI-9. There we discuss in greater detail the basic difference between point and area targets, according to which the types of attack can be subdivided into point-attack and area-attack procedures.

The individual types of point-attack follow from the requirement that the bomber fly as slowly as possible over the target, so that it may have rather small residual energy there. If, in spite of this, the bomber is to return to its takeoff field without a proper stopover, then after dropping its bombs over the target it must be propelled by its own motor until it has acquired sufficient speed to get home on the corresponding energy. Thus we arrive at procedures for attack involving two propulsions and return home, which consists essentially in having the bomber, after being catapulted at the home base, accelerated only until it acquires enough energy to bring it over the target. There it releases and turns at the lowest possible speed, then starts its motor with the residual store of fuel, to get up enough energy for the home trip, and lands back at its home base. Very large quantities of fuel are required for this double propulsion, so that this procedure can be used only for limited ranges of attack (up to 6,000 kilometers) and limited bomb load. Point-attacks over greater distances, or with target bomb loads than in this first procedure, are possible if the bomber can land not too far from the target and take on new fuel.

For the point-attack procedure with two driving periods, partial turning and auxiliary point, the bomber is again accelerated after catapult from the home base, until the required energy carries it just to the target. Then it releases, turns through the required angle at least possible flight speed, starts its motor with the small residue of fuel on board, to get the small amount of energy which carries it to the auxiliary field not too far from the target. It lands there and takes on new fuel. With this, it takes off again in normal fashion and returns to the home base; it has the possibility of making further bombing attacks on the way home.

If a point-attack is to be carried out over a larger distance, or with a very great bomb load, and there is no possible auxiliary landing place near the target, then rocket technique, as seen at the present time, gives no possibility of retrieving the bomber and bringing it back to its home field. If attack on the target seems more important than the bomber itself (which has only relatively small material value), then there is the possibility of sacrificing the bomber after the attack. The procedure of point-attack with a single propulsion period and sacrifice of the bomber is, in principle, applicable to all points on the earth's surface. It is naturally to be applied to attacks on and targets of special significance as, for example, the surprise destruction of a government building and the governing group assembled there to the killing of a single, especially important enemy person, to sinking large enemy transports or warships, blocking of important avenues of commerce (canals or straits), and to similar special cases; this is less because of the loss of the aircraft than of the more valuable pilot.

For Procedures of Attack on an Area

The most obvious procedure for the area-attack, with single propulsive system period and return home, consists of the bomber being catapulted from its home base and then driven until it gets sufficient energy to get to the vicinity of the target, turn and get back home. The turn path uses up very large amounts of energy so that this attack procedure remains limited to small distances and bomb loads.

Area-attack over great distances is very much simplified if an auxiliary field exists not too far from the target, so that the bomber can land and take on new fuel for the return trip. In this case the area-attack goes as follows:

After release, the bomber makes a partial turn through an angle less than 180 degrees (this requires smaller energy consumption than for a complete turn), then flies to the auxiliary field on its residual energy. This area-attack with single propulsion, partial turn and auxiliary field is applicable to all distances on the earth. It assumes, however, that within at most a few thousand kilometers from the target area, there is a suitable auxiliary field for landing and which has takeoff apparatus. In view of the large number of possible targets for area-attack, this requirement can be fulfilled only in exceptional cases.

The value of the auxiliary point can vary considerably, not only according to its distance from the target, but also because of the size of the required angle of turn. Since large angles of turns are much more harmful than great distances, an obvious idea is to provide auxiliary points beyond all foreseeable targets, e.g., beyond the two population concentrations outside of Europe (North America and Southeast Asia), say, on the Mariannas in the Pacific Ocean or on the islands of that ocean off the Mexican coast; or to secure a single auxiliary point at the antipodes of the home base. That is, in New Zealand or on the islands east of it. This auxiliary point at the antipodes can always be reached by straight-line flight without turning, no matter what point on earth is attacked. Its distance from the target can be very large. On this discussion is based the method of area-attack with single propulsion and auxiliary point at the antipodes. Such a single auxiliary point also has the advantage that it can be easily fully equipped to enable aircraft also to make bombing attacks on their journey back to the home base, and that its island location can be easily protected against enemy attacks;

against the most dangerous attacks by enemy fleets or units, this could be done by rocket bombers.

If such an auxiliary point at the antipodes is not available, area-attacks over large distances can be carried out by having the bomber after release fly a straight course all the way around the earth until it reaches the home base. This is the procedure for attack with single propulsion and circumnavigation of the globe.

Summarizing: All possible procedures for area-attack coincide with what happens up to bomb release; they differ only in the manner of bringing the bomber home after it releases the bomb load.

This is a typical example of the thoroughness of the Saenger study and it goes on page after page in great detail. In the final analysis, for the operation of the bomber two basic factors had to be considered—the bomb load must be curtailed in favor of distance and, conversely, the larger the bomb load, the shorter the distance over which the space bomber could deliver it. There were, of course, other considerations, such as the direction in which the flight took place. This was critical in that the bomber was either given a plus push in an easterly direction, because of the earth's rotation, or a minus rotational effect if the vehicle flew in a westerly direction. If the craft flew directly north or south, the earth's motion neither added to nor subtracted from the velocity.

Militarily, one of the soundest aspects of Dr. Saenger's arguments for the Antipodal Bomber was the significance of the explosive force of the bombs themselves when dropped from such extreme altitudes and at such fantastic speeds. In the case of an area attack which, of course, would be on a target such as a city or a large industrial complex, the bombs would be dropped from an altitude of around 30 to 100 miles and at speeds of more than 14,000 miles per hour. The pilot would not see the target at the time of bombs away, for his craft would be at too great a distance over the horizon. For instance, to hit New York the pilot would have to release his bomb load over Nevada or Utah.

One of the really extraordinary aspects of the missions which were planned for the space bomber was the simplicity of the navigational techniques to be employed.

For obtaining his position over any particular spot on the earth,

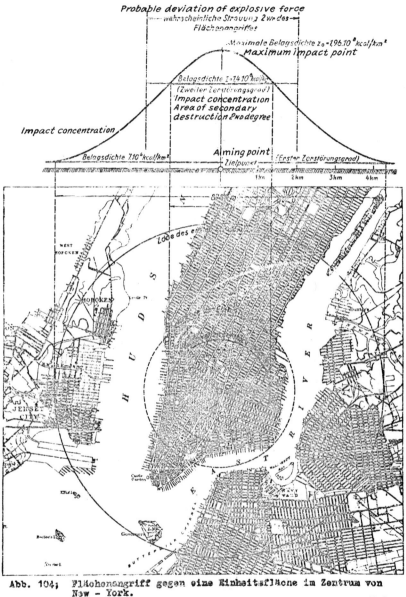

Probable deviation of explosive force

wahrscheinliche Strauung 2w des
Flächenangriffes

Maximale Belagsdichte $z_0 = 1,96.10^8 \, kcal/km^2$
Maximum impact point

Belagsdichte $z = 1,4.10^8 \, kcal/km^2$
(Zweiter Zerstörungsgrad)
Impact concentration
Area of secondary
destruction 2nd degree

Impact concentration

Belagsdichte $7.10^8 \, kcal/km^2$
Aiming point
Zielpunkt
(Erster Zerstörungsgrad)

1km 2km 3km 4km

Abb. 104; Flächenangriff gegen eine Einheitsfläche im Zentrum von New - York.
Plan of attack against a surface target at the center of New York

Diagram shows the mathematically computed impact points for an Antipodal Bomber attack on New York City. The graph at the top of the map indicates the predicted concentration of the explosive force (the rising peak) which would have been delivered to Manhattan—the mid point of this metropolis. A captured Luftwaffe document.

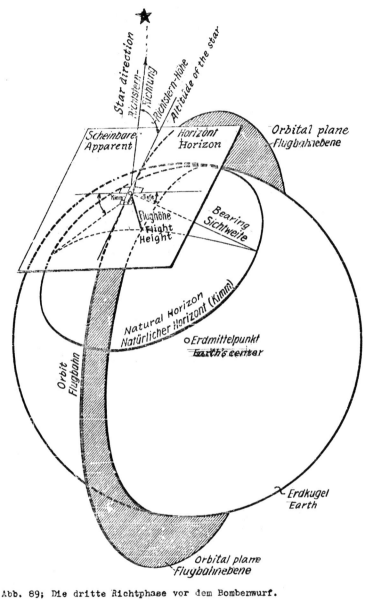

Star direction
Richtstern-
Richtung
Richtstern-Höhe
Altitude of the star

Scheinbare
Apparent

Horizont
Horizon

Orbital plane
Flugbahnebene

Kimm Tiefe

Flughöhe
Flight
Height

Bearing
Sichtweite

Natural Horizon
Natürlicher Horizont (Kimm)

o Erdmittelpunkt
Earth's center

Orbit
Flugbahn

Erdkugel
Earth

Orbital plane
Flugbahnebene

Abb. 89; Die dritte Richtphase vor dem Bombenwurf.
*The third directional phase before
dropping the bomb.*

133

The above **diagram**, taken from captured Luftwaffe files at the end of World War II, shows how the Antipodal Bomber pilot would have determined his position and his altitude in order to release his bombs at the proper moment in space.

the pilot was to take along a very simple sextant with which he would take three sightings on the horizon at evenly spaced intervals of 120 degrees (this is deduced by dividing three into 360), in order to determine his altitude by triangulation techniques. The second bit of information needed by the antipodal navigator would be the direction of the horizontal plane in which he was flying. This would be determined by the sighting of any one of the many stars lying in the plane of the target area. He would also be able to determine his velocity by referring to a star and observing the speed at which it crossed the vertical cross hairs in the sextant. As a matter of interest, this technique of navigation has been tried in Project Gemini. As a result of these tests, the sextant, which is hundreds of years old, will also be used as one of several navigational techniques in the flights of the astronauts to the moon. In the latter case, this is desirable because it will represent a saving in weight which is very critical on the moon mission. In addition, the sextant is extremely simple, thus very reliable.

Although time was the greatest factor in the Allies' favor, there were other factors which thwarted the efforts of scientists such as Dr. Saenger, such as the lack of imagination on the part of the men who advised Hitler and, of course, Hitler himself. He was never convinced that any of the super weapons being designed should actually be built until the last desperate hours. By then, the fate of Germany had been sealed. The Allies can also be grateful that the strategy of the men who conducted the air war for them was right. By keeping the pressure of aerial bombardment on Germany's factories, transportation facilities, and airfields, she was rendered helpless.

In retrospect, it is awesome speculation indeed to wonder what might have happened if the imagination and creativeness of men such as Saenger had been encouraged to any great extent, so that the Antipodal Bomber or similar weapons would have been ready to play a role in the planned conquest of the world in the decade between 1935 and 1945!

6

Kamikaze — Suicide on Wings

In their last desperate hours, the Germans had considered the use of ramming tactics as a means of combating Allied air power. Although they had gone as far as recruiting volunteers, who responded in significant numbers, the scheme went no further than the thought stage and ultimately all of the volunteers returned to their old organizations to await inevitable surrender as World War II drew to an end. In the truest sense, the German plans were actually not suicidal, but carefully calculated tactics to give the pilot a reasonable chance to survive a plunge into an enemy aircraft. Several devices were conceived to permit him this chance. One was an ejection seat for his fighter, actuated by an impact switch which would throw him clear of both aircraft, once contact was made. Another German tactic simply called for the pilot to maneuver his plane on a collision course with a bomber victim, then, after feeling assured of his aim, he would bail out of his aircraft, which would plummet on to seal the fate of the bomber and its crew.

On the other hand, the Japanese Army and Navy Air Forces, in their desperate hours, chose to organize large numbers of suicide squadrons. These met with considerable success, to which many men of the U.S. Navy will attest.

On October 19, 1944, Admiral Ohnishi, commander of the Royal Japanese Air Forces, stationed in the Philippines, met with several aides to discuss the bleak course which the war was taking for the Japanese forces. During these discussions, he brought up an idea which he had been considering for many months. American aircraft carriers had wrested control of the skies from their Japanese adversaries to such a degree that only the direst of measures could possibly turn the tide of war in the eyes of the ranking Japanese admirals. To Ohnishi there remained only one hope to thwart the American strategy—suicide attacks on the United States carriers. At this hastily summoned meeting the admiral outlined his plan in detail for his wing commanders. The objective called for the initial use of the famous Zero fighters, each fitted with a 500-pound bomb. These were to plunge into the decks of the American carriers, knocking them out of commission, or perhaps sinking them, if the targets reached with great precision were the carriers' most vulnerable spots.

The big task which lay ahead for the commanders who would organize these operations would be the securing of volunteers. At no other time in history had a group of men been asked to perform such an unusual and suicidal duty. There are, of course, cases on file in the records of the armed forces of every country where men individually, or in groups, have volunteered to undertake crucial missions in the defense of their country. However, there have been few, if any, circumstances where such large numbers of men have volunteered for a duty which meant sure death. In most cases, there has been some semblance of a chance for survival. In the operation which was about to unfold with the Japanese Naval Air Force, agreement to serve was to volunteer for death.

The name "Kamikaze" was given to the operation and has become a rather firmly entrenched part of our English vernacular. Although the designation has taken on a connotation of absurd recklessness with regard to ending one's life, in Japanese "Kamikaze" means "Divine Wind." It seems that the word "Kamikaze" stems historically from a military operation during which Kubla Khan organized a Mongol armada with which he intended to invade and conquer the islands of Japan. In the midst of near success, a great

Re-enactment of a typical Kamikaze ceremony by former Japanese pilots.

typhoon was spawned off the coast of Japan which scattered his ships asunder, thus thwarting what appeared to be sure victory. The Japanese interpreted this as a sign of heavenly intervention and credited the salvation of the empire to Kamikaze—Divine Wind.

The first assembly of pilots to brief them on the plans for the organization of Kamikaze units, the commanders were apprehensive that the number of volunteers resulting from this "rallying talk" might not be sufficient to attain the strength which they desired. Admiral Ohnishi's audience sat in rapt silence as he related his plan, which could have profound effect on their fate. After explaining these drastic measures to the group, he asked that all of those who desired to volunteer raise their hands. A hand of every single one of those assembled for the briefing went up in unison. The admiral appeared visibly relieved upon taking note of the number of hands. The first unit was given the name "Shimpu."

The first opportunity to launch a Kamikaze attack came just a few short hours after the first group had volunteered, when a large segment of the American fleet was sighted. However, owing to the great distance between them and the American vessels, a decision was made to hold back the attacking group until their targets came to within a more favorable range.

With the break of dawn the following day, the twenty-three Kamikazes were alerted to get ready for an attack on another

American task force which had been sighted by scout planes in the vicinity of Leyte. The preparations for the attack were unbelievably normal, almost nonchalant, with the exception of a brief ceremony which involved lining up to drink water from an urn left by Admiral Ohnishi for these occasions.

The comrades of these aviation notables who were standing by to wish them farewell began to sing an ancient Japanese song, which cast a solemn air over the airfield. The lyrics of the song are as follows:

> If I go away to sea,
> I shall return a corpse awash;
> If duty calls me to the mountain,
> A verdant award will be my pall;
> Thus for the sake of the Emperor
> I will not die peacefully at home.

The Kamikazes took off for the locality which had been reported to them by the scout planes as being infested with American warships. Ironically, after a lengthy search, they found nothing in that area and had to return to their base. The pilots who should have been dead by the hour at which they returned had been spared for another day.

Several other abortive sorties were flown as the American fleet lurked in nearby waters. Unable to find their intended targets, these pilots with a volunteered fatal destiny were forced to return to their base again and again, their missions incomplete. The morale of the Kamikaze unit sank to a low ebb, which is rather unimaginable when one considers that these pilots were demoralized by the fact that they had not had any occasion to destroy themselves in a plunge to the deck of an American aircraft carrier.

The first successful Kamikaze attack was led by the first man to volunteer. He had been named commander of the first unit—Lieutenant Seki. After trying in vain for four consecutive days, he took off in search of his prey in the waters west of the Philippine Islands.

The American force was a rather formidable one, which included a prized carrier. At 10:45 A.M. Lieutenant Seki, who was serving as the leader of a flight of five bomb-laden Zeros, escorted by four other Zeros, spotted the enemy task force. Seki gave the signal for the plunge after each pilot had agreed on his target. He flew through a seemingly impenetrable wall of antiaircraft fire, until his airplane found its mark on the deck of the *St. Lo* at 10:45 A.M. He was followed seconds later by his wingman. Several violent explosions rocked the carrier and she sank immediately. According to official U.S. Navy files, five Kamikazes did impact on American vessels on that date, with one of these confirmed as being the carrier *St. Lo*. The first Japanese suicide sortie had been a resounding success.

The following day, other Kamikaze units were sent out after the sighting of an American fleet buildup in the same general area. This group did not meet with complete success. Only the carrier *Suwanee* was reported officially as having been damaged as a result of the attack. Not even the Japanese escort fighters returned safely from this mission, because of the tremendous opposition they encountered at the hands of American fighters and antiaircraft fire.

The Japanese missions continued to mount in intensity in the area of the Philippine Islands until by January 1945 the Kamikazes had sunk sixteen American ships, some of which were carriers. They severely damaged seventy-seven others. These actions had become an object of grave concern to the admirals of the U.S. Navy. Nevertheless, the United States emerged victorious in the battles that took place in the vicinity of the Philippines, and the Japanese were forced to withdraw their forces to other areas in order to continue opposing American naval might which was being brought to bear.

In withdrawing from the Philippines, a decision was made by the Japanese high command to continue the attacks from Formosa, the Japanese islands proper, and Okinawa, where hundreds of other pilots had volunteered to fly the one-way missions. From these new bases the attacks continued relentlessly and vessel after vessel became victim of the suicidal plunges.

Although she was having significant success, Japan was also paying a prohibitive price, not only in terms of the pilots and aircraft lost in the Kamikaze operations, but she was also losing a large number of the escort aircraft. These planes were ultimately intended for

suicide operations, but by being shot down in the course of escorting the Kamikazes, they could, naturally, play no role of significance
in defeating the enemy. The lives of some of the Kamikazes were
also spent futilely, for they were shot down prior to reaching their
objectives, either by the protective screen of fighters which the
American carrier force kept constantly overhead, or by the very
accurate fire laid down by the gunners aboard the vessels under
attack.

One of the major reasons why the Japanese aircraft, such as the
Zeros, and other similar makes, were shot down was because they
were so slow that their favorable attributes—particularly their
maneuverability—proved to be useless on a suicide plunge. The
same versatility had paid great dividends when engaging American
fighters in dog fights. The Kamikaze plunge was a straight-line
flight, in order to gather maximum speed and to expose as small a
target as possible to the gunners on the decks of the enemy vessels
marked for destruction.

The simplest answer to make the Kamikazes a success was for
the Japanese to find an aircraft which could outspeed the protective
fighters of the American fleet and also would give the enemy gunners a minimum of time during which to train their deadly weapons
accurately on the attackers. A young ensign of the Royal Japanese
Navy, named Ohta, had given thought to perfecting the use of
suicidal strategy as early as 1943, because of the bleak course of the
war from the Japanese point of view. In August 1944 the high command of the Japanese Navy began to look with greater interest on
his project, which he had so far pursued rather informally on his
own. In late 1944, Ensign Ohta submitted plans to the Naval Aero-
nautic Depot at Yokosuka for the building of an extremely small
rocket-propelled aircraft of great simplicity, with small stub wings.

Ohta's concept called for the tiny craft to be carried under the
belly of a Betty bomber. The Betty would carry the flying bomb
within twelve or fourteen miles of the enemy's carrier and drop it
for a final plunge to the objective. In order to assure the maximum
chance of success, three rocket units were to be mounted in the tail
of each new Kamikaze aircraft. These would propel it to amazing

speeds—considerably faster than those of the swiftest United States carrier fighters. Sensing sure defeat without the introduction of something revolutionary, the Japanese Navy approved Ohta's plan without reservation.

The craft was given the name Ohka (Cherry Blossom) and was ordered into production in late 1944. The project was so secret that only a few select persons in the Japanese Navy department who had direct concern with the program were informed about it. Even the Kamikaze pilots, who were waiting their turns to fly missions in the archaic Zeros, did not know of its existence.

The Ohka was a mere twenty feet in length and had a wing span of sixteen and one-half feet. The little human coffin could fly in excess of 600 miles per hour, which was easily 150 miles per hour faster than the fastest fighter in the fleet, or the land-based interceptors. In addition to speed, its only other asset was the fact that

The Baka bomb cutaway showing the general layout of the aircraft.

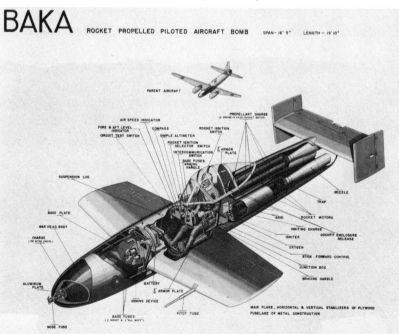

Technicians of the American Air Force are shown examining one of the Baka bombs abandoned on the island of Okinawa. Note the 2200-pound bomb which served as the nose contour of the aircraft. The very simple sight just in front of the windshield was used to aim the aircraft with its bomb and human guidance system at the target.

this manned projectile carried 2,645 pounds of explosives—a lethal package in anyone's military arsenal. The front of the fuselage, from the cockpit forward, was literally a bomb to which the rear of the fuselage and wings were attached. The destructive power of the Ohka human rocket bomb would be more than five times that of the Zeros—a distressing attribute as far as the men of the U.S. Navy were concerned.

As the Ohkas began to roll off the assembly lines, advanced preparations for their use were being made.

In September 1944 Captain Okamura was placed in charge of the first Ohka squadron and the unit was formed at an air base located northeast of Tokyo. Okamura had long been an advocate of Kamikaze tactics and he himself had volunteered for the project at a much earlier date.

One of the agonizing aspects of the training program for Ohka duty was the fact that it was more than six months in length. To the

The Baka was powered by three solid rocket motors mounted as shown here. The motors only burned for a short duration but sufficiently long to propel the little craft to phenomenal speeds.

prospective Ohka pilot this would be the earliest possible date to which he could look forward for his death plunge into an American ship.

The Ohkas were to be committed to action for the first time on March 20, 1945, against a large American task force. Sixteen of them were to be dispatched against the enemy ships, slung beneath their Betty bombers' fuselages. The first group of mother aircraft took to the air at 11:35 A.M., accompanied by their fighter escort, numbering fifty-five.

At two o'clock in the afternoon, the Bettys were attacked by fifty U.S. Navy fighters, which had been flying protective cover for the carrier force. The interceptors went first for the Bettys, with their lethal cargo on board. The bombers, unable to maneuver or take evasive action, owing to the weight of the Ohkas slung under their bellies, were hapless victims of the interceptors' machine-gun fire. The entire Kamikaze group was lost prior to any chance of release onto the American targets—a rather inept beginning for the Ohka rocket bomb.

After this first contact with the new rocket-powered menace, the men of the U.S. Navy promptly branded the Ohka as the Baka bomb, which, translated from the Japanese, means "fool bomb."

Even though this first effort was quite a dismal failure, the Baka bomb aircraft went on to wreak havoc on many an American ship as the "human guidance" system quite accurately assured impact against vessel after vessel.

The Japanese also gave thought to the use of the Baka as an inter-

Cockpit of the Baka bomb. Note the absolute minimum number of flight instruments and the simplicity of the cockpit layout.

ceptor. This version would have involved suicide while climbing vertically, instead at the end of the downward plunge, which became so famous during the Kamikaze operations. The American B-29's were flying mission after mission almost entirely without opposition from the Japanese Air Force. This was owing primarily to the high altitudes at which these American aircraft were capable of operating and the Zeros' inability to attain such heights. Again in desperation, the thoughts of the Japanese turned to suicidal means of destroying the enemy. The Baka interceptor would have been fitted with a rocket engine having a longer-thrust duration than the original Bakas. As a result, the mother ship would lug the Bakas to altitudes where they could loiter at a considerable distance from their prey until they could opportunely drop their charges for an attack on a formation of B-29's. Upon release, the Baka would scream toward the enemy aircraft, ramming into the most convenient target with an accompanying crescendo of the explosive power which she would carry.

Like the efforts of the Germans in the last hours of World War II, when the conventional methods ceased to be effective, the Japanese were forced, in desperation, to resort to unorthodox weapons and unbelievable demands upon the men who manned them. Again history repeated itself and, although the methods of Kamikaze met with some success, they were too little and too late to influence the final outcome of the war in the Pacific. However, they took their toll in American vessels before the dropping of the atomic bombs in August 1945 sealed the fate of the empire and Japan capitulated.

One of the many captured Baka bombs found on the island of Okinawa at the end of World War II. Note the cherry blossom which was the insignia of one of the Kamikaze units.

The final tally at the end of World War II showed 322 Allied ships sunk, or damaged, because of Kamikaze operations.

The Baka bomb was the only effort on the part of the Japanese to harness the power of the rocket engine to a winged vehicle during World War II. They did, however, negotiate with the Germans to build the formidable ME-163 fighter for their own use. The plans for its construction were en route from Germany as early as 1944, aboard a Japanese submarine. The vessel was intercepted and sunk, carrying with it the designs for a fighter which could have offered tremendous opposition to the fleets of B-29's of the U.S. Air Force, which played such an important role in defeating the Japanese. Again, hindsight makes for curious speculation as to what might have been had these devastating weapons been brought into the fray at an earlier period.

A Baka bomb explodes on the deck of an American carrier. Note fragments of the craft that skipped off the deck, splashing into the ocean to the left.

7

Crossing the New Frontier

One of the almost invariable results of warfare is the fact that scientific research and development and important breakthroughs are accelerated manyfold. World War II was no exception, for it was during this period that aviation made its greatest strides. But, as might well be expected, these breakthroughs were devoted exclusively to increasing the capabilities of military aircraft.

The speeds of the propeller-driven fighters were pushed higher and higher until they were in excess of the 500 miles per hour, which was considered to be an insurmountable hurdle by many engineers a few short years before. The Germans were breaking down the speed barrier at a phenomenal rate in their newly-introduced jets and rocket aircraft. While flying in these previously unexplored speed ranges, pilots, under certain circumstances, had begun to encounter a strange new phenomenon called compressibility. It seems that, on several occasions, in the furor of dogfights with enemy aircraft, with their eyes glued to their opponents' whereabouts, they would let their minds wander momentarily from the airplane's instrument panel. In the wild chases that ensued they frequently found themselves in vertical dives, with full throttle, to assure that their foes would not elude them. When the time came to recover from such dives, they were startled to find that the controls would not respond to their efforts to pull out, and the aircraft would buffet and shudder violently.

Heini Dittmar, the first ME-163 test pilot, experienced this uncomfortable sensation while flying the ME-163 to achieve a record speed on October 2, 1941. Events surrounding the record run were of a most secretive nature. The world was not even permitted to know that such a remarkable event had taken place. However, the ME-163 was flying horizontally when the compressibility phenomenon set in. An excerpt from Dittmar's formal report best describes the sensation: "My speedometer soon read 910 kilometers [565 miles per hour] and kept on climbing, soon topping the 1,000 kilometers-per-hour mark. Then the needle began to waver; there was sudden vibration in the elevons and the next moment the aircraft went into an uncontrollable dive, causing strong negative acceleration. I immediately cut the rocket and for a few moments thought that I had really had it at last. Then, just as suddenly, the controls reacted again and I eased the aircraft out of the dive. The so-called mach penomenon that I had just experienced was the first knock on the door of the sound barrier which my aircraft had not been built to penetrate."

At the end of World War II, these flights, which had knocked at the door of the sound barrier, would represent the next formidable hurdle in aviation to be surmounted. The chief concern of the Americans who planned to pursue advanced aviation research was the problem of who would underwrite the costs. The mighty air armadas which had been assembled for the global showdown during the war were now being reduced to scrap heaps. In most cases, the people of the United States were more interested in the demobolization efforts than in any new aeronautical developments. But to a select few there was a critical need to keep at least a token research effort alive, and one of the major objectives in their minds was to surmount that next barrier in aviation which the Germans had come so close to conquering prior to the war's end—compressibility.

One thing was sure in the opinion of those who speculated on the crossing of the sonic threshold. Propeller-driven aircraft would

Preparing for the first American manned rocket flight, at March Field, in August, 1941, are the late Dr. Clark Milliken, Dr. Martin Summerfield, the late Dr. Theodore von Karman, founder of Aerojet-General Corporation, Dr. Frank Malina, and Captain Homer A. Boushey, the first American rocket pilot.

never be able to penetrate the barrier because of the intense vibrations which occurred at the tips of the prop blades.

There were two schools of thought in United States aviation circles regarding the selection of a power plant. The representatives of the U.S. Army Air Force were in favor of rocket propulsion. The representatives of the National Advisory Committee for Aeronautics and the U.S. Navy favored jet power for the new endeavor.

However, it was one thing to indulge in theoretical speculation about an exotic new airplane which could cross the heretofore impenetrable wall, and it was quite another to find a sponsor for such an undertaking, especially in the atmosphere which then prevailed in the United States for the reduction of Air Force personnel in the shortest possible time, and to forget about weapons of war. It had been difficult enough to spur on exotic and usually very expensive new research in the United States, even under the pressures of war (the atomic bomb being a notable exception). Her research in rocketry was paltry in contrast to that of the Germans. For instance, only two types of rocket aircraft were flown in the United States during World War II. Although they were notable in boldness, they were rather amateurish and makeshift in comparison with the German products.

The first airplane to fly under rocket power in the United States was a commercially-produced Ercoupe flown by Captain Homer Boushey, who was assigned to the staff of Dr. Theodore von Karman, a world-renowned mathematician and aeronautical engineer. Von Karman was in charge of research subjects conducted in behalf of the Army Air Force under the auspices of the California Institute of Technology.

The little craft was fitted with six solid rockets, mounted under the wings. The first flight was made with the piston-driven engine producing the primary power and the rockets serving only as an auxiliary source. Boushey later made takeoffs with the airplane's piston engine inoperative, and using the solid rockets alone. The major point of these experiments was to prove the practicability of rocket-assisted takeoff units for heavily-laden aircraft in order to get them out of short fields. To this end they were very beneficial. However, they made little, if any, contribution to the further development of power plants for aircraft.

The second American effort to employ rocket engines for propelling aircraft occurred on the fifth day of July 1944. A sleek little flying wing-type aircraft made its appearance on the dry lake at

Captain Homer Boushey makes the first rocket-powered flight in an aircraft in the United States. On this particular flight the propeller was also furnishing power, along with the solid rockets attached to the underside of the wings. On subsequent flights, Boushey made takeoffs using rocket thrust alone.

The MX-324 flying wing was the first liquid rocket-powered aircraft to fly in the United States. The pilot of the aircraft lay in a prone position to fly the unorthodox little craft.

Muroc, California. It was labeled the MX-324 and was powered by a 200-pound-thrust liquid rocket engine. The thrust output of the engine, however, was too feeble to permit the aircraft to take off under its own power. To resolve this problem and to acquire aeronautical data on the aircraft design itself, the plane was towed to an altitude of around 14,000 feet by a P-38 fighter. There it was released. Shortly thereafter, the pilot fired up the rocket engine and the craft flew for approximately four minutes.

All of the flights of the MX-324 were conducted in the strictest of secrecy.

In retrospect, all this seems rather absurd at the war's end, for the Germans had accomplished more notable achievements in 1937 and they were also in a position to launch hundreds of rocket fighters years prior to that. In short, the United States seems to have been extremely lethargic at that time in exploring new and exotic areas of research. However, there were groups of dedicated scientists and military men who persevered, and it was the members of one of these who were destined to achieve the newest dimension of flight —the crossing of the sonic barrier.

Obviously prompted—or alarmed—by the aeronautical events which were being witnessed in the skies over Germany, the U.S. Congress in 1944 appropriated funds for an aircraft research program. The intent was to build flying aeronautical laboratories as a means of solving some of the more difficult aviation riddles. Foremost among the puzzlers of this period was the sound barrier. Almost everyone associated with aeronautics was talking about this mysterious new realm of flight.

Before the year 1944 slipped into history, the U.S. Army Air Force had signed a contract with the Bell Aircraft Corporation for three airplanes which were destined to become the first of the flying laboratories which Congress had approved. These aircraft were to be designated X-1—the X denoting experimental and the 1 indicating the first in that series. All three airplanes were to be identical, except for minor differences in the thickness of the wings.

There were many specifications written into the Bell contract for these unusual airplanes. They should be designed to carry a large instrument payload which would include cameras for obtaining various kinds of information within the X-1 itself, as well as recorders and telemetering devices for documenting and transmitting data on the performance of the craft in flight. This data would include air-foil pressure distribution and points of stress on the airplane as measured by strain gauges. Other devices would measure acceleration and control stick forces.

Perhaps the most stringent aspect of the contract was the provision that called for delivery of the aircraft within a year. This was considered essential in case the war had become more prolonged. It was hoped that this experimental vehicle would furnish valuable information which could be applied to the development of more advanced aircraft to be hurled against the enemy. Certainly, in that period the Allies needed something more formidable than the propeller-driven fighters which they had used thus far to combat the German jets and rocket fighters.

Bell's contract also called for a demonstration of the following minimum performance requirements, as extracted from the contract. First, an 8-G pullout, that is, a stress of eight times the normal force of gravity, at an indicated air speed not exceeding 500 miles per hour. An 8-G pullout at minimum air speed. A proof of the specified endurance at rated thrust, and takeoff and climb to 35,000 feet under its own power. Finally, it must respond satisfactorily to controls at a speed of mach number 0.8. (The mach number is named

The X-1 being mated to the bomb bay of the B-29 for the first assault on the sound barrier.

for a German scientist, Ernst Mach, who devised the system of designating speeds in reference to the speed of sound.) The speed of sound is not constant. It decreases with altitude and temperature, from 763 miles per hour at sea level to about 660 miles per hour at 40,000 feet. A mach number of one is the speed of sound at any altitude. Therefore, mach number 0.8 would be 80 per cent of the speed of sound at any altitude. An instrument known as a mach meter, which automatically compensates for altitude and temperature, is employed to register such readings.

The X-1 was designed and manufactured in record time. It was delivered in 1945, just after the end of World War II. In January 1946 the first shakedown flights of the bullet-shaped rocket plane began. First it was put through a series of gliding flights. These were accomplished by lugging the X-1 aloft, slung beneath the belly of a B-29 bomber, which had been modified for the role. One of the potential hazards which the engineers had considered was that the X-1 might leave the bomb bay of the mother aircraft in an unstable attitude and collide with the B-29's tail surface.

In the first drops, however, their fears proved to be ill-founded as the projectile-like X-1 dropped vertically and very stably from the B-29. Further to assure that this would not occur, the inboard propellers of the B-29 were feathered (that is, stopped turning, with the narrowest side of the blade headed into the wind). This procedure was intended to reduce the chances that the turbulant air generated by the inboard propellers might disturb the path of the smaller aircraft's fall as it left the bomber. A total of ten successful

The X-1, the first of a series of experimental aircraft developed solely to obtain aeronautical data which would be applied to the design of futuristic aircraft with a practical role.

glide flights were made, which was convincing enough for Bell's engineers. The airplanes were sent on their way to Edwards Air Force Base in California, where the power-plant installations were completed.

Edwards is the U.S. Air Force Flight Test Center for experimental aircraft. It possesses one of the world's largest natural runways in the dry lake bed which is adjacent to the base. This field is particularly suited for planes, such as the X-1, which might require a vast landing area because of its speed and precarious flight characteristics, especially when it had been probing the aeronautical unknowns.

The first X-1 arrived at Edwards on October 7, 1946, and the wheels were set in motion to prepare the craft for its first powered flight. On the morning of December 9, 1946, the rocket plane was hoisted aboard a B-29 which, before the day's end, had lifted its charge to altitude, where it was released. After this, the pilot fired the rocket engine, which propelled the sleek air-searing projectile to a respectable speed, but not sufficiently high to startle the aeronautical world. The people managing the X-1 program had decided at the outset that the flight schedule for this new airplane would proceed on a very methodical basis, with each flight bolstering its performance in very small increments.

The original power plant for the X-1, built by Reaction Motors of Denville, New Jersey, was a four-chamber rocket engine which used liquid oxygen and alcohol as fuels. These were fed to the ignition chambers under pressure by the use of nitrogen gas. The X-1 pilot had the alternative of firing all of the rocket chambers simultaneously, or he could fire them individually, or in various combinations. Each chamber generated a thrust of 1,500 pounds. If the pilot decided on a particular flight to fire these one at a time, the first spurt of power would be 1,500 pounds; the next would increase this to 3,000 pounds; and so on until he had fired the last chamber, giving him a total of 6,000 pounds of thrust. The tanks of this unusual bird held 5,000 pounds of fuel. With all chambers going, it required only 150 seconds to empty them.

One of the several new features of the X-1 which surprised many engineers was its straight-edge wings. This was particularly difficult for many of them to understand because of the success of the German ME-163, which had swept wings. Also, this straight form seemed to defy other research data which were available as a result of the flights of the winged version of the V-2 rocket. This weapon of war, with its swept wings, had flown beyond the speed of sound, and the Germans had considered it for manned flight, with the designation of A-9.

During the summer of 1946, great strides were made on the X-1 project. Captain Charles (Chuck) Yeager had taken over as test pilot for the Air Force and had completed his checkout in the X-1, in a series of nonpowered drops from the mother B-29. Every flight without power meant gliding back to the dry lake bed. Then came the time when Yeager was ready for the first powered flight. The plan for this mission called for the eager young test pilot to fly with full propellant tanks. He was merely supposed to acquaint himself with the way the airplane handled, and to fly at a moderate speed, cutting in only one rocket chamber at a time. He had been emphatically cautioned not to exceed mach 0.8, or 80 per cent of the speed of sound.

On the morning of the flight, the chubby craft was wheeled down into the pit, which had been recessed into the cement of the Edwards flight line. This permitted rolling the B-29 in over the smaller craft. The brilliant orange-colored little bird was then hoisted up into the bomb bay of the B-29, which hovered over it like a lurking

To conserve the rocket aircraft's limited fuel supply, a B-29 bomber was modified to accommodate the X-1 in its bomb bay, from which it was dropped. The speed of the bomber, plus the altitude from which the rocket aircraft was dropped, meant easier attainment of the goal.

giant parent. With its thirty-one-foot-long fuselage and the twenty-eight-foot wing span, this sturdy rocket plane looked rather insignificant in contrast to the mother ship, which completely engulfed it.

The ground crewmen began to load the highly explosive fuel. While the fuel was being poured into its tanks, the sides of the fuselage took on a frosty external appearance as the 300-degree-below-zero liquid oxygen literally froze it inside and out.

Finally, when all the items on the ground check list were found to be okay, the lumbering B-29 taxied cautiously out to the runway and took to the air. After climbing to the prescribed altitude of 21,000 feet, all was made ready for the drop. After what appeared to Yeager to be an eternity, the little beast was dropped. Shortly thereafter, the pilot fired the number-three rocket chamber, which came alive with a roar. As the thrust of the engine mounted, Yeager slipped his versatile charge into a graceful, slow roll, a maneuver which was not intended in the flight plan. In the midst of the roll, the engine stopped abruptly. This was caused by the sloshing of the fuels in the tanks. After righting the aircraft, Yeager ignited the other engines in random sequence—and all roared to life. By this time, the orange meteor was screaming straight up, and the youthful pilot, in a wild state of exhilaration, was doing all he could to keep it under the prescribed mach 0.8. He pulled the nose of the runaway craft through until it appeared as though he would complete a full loop. At this point, he looked very carefully at his mach meter. It read an unbelievable .83—and the speed continued to build, finally reaching .85. Yeager decided at this point that the only thing that would thwart the speed of his runaway craft would be to shut off the engine—which he did immediately. He then began the long glide back to the dry lake, jubilant over his initial powered flight in the first of the X-planes.

After several more powered flights which pushed the mach numbers higher and higher, Yeager and the engineering crew were sure that the glistening bolt of lightning was ready for the sonic barrier. Not everyone, including many world-renowned scientists, shared their optimism, and the cynics of that group were predicting dire results for the man who dared try. Even wind-tunnel data, acquired in the earliest stages of design, seemed to indicate that this particular aircraft could not conquer the mysterious barrier.

Early October 1947 saw the successful completion of an eighth powered flight by Yeager, and he was still busy trying to convince the X-1 project officials that the time was at hand for a crack at the barrier.

Finally, the green light was given for the ninth flight, which was scheduled for October 14, 1947.

The day of the important flight arrived and the base sprang alive with a bustle of activity. Although the outward signs were scarcely noticeable, there was tension in the air, for man had never deliberately taken this step in aviation before. Many of the project people who were very well informed on aeronautical matters remembered all too vividly the death of Geoffrey de Haviland, the British test pilot who had been killed not too long prior to this, when he knocked at the door of the sonic wall. His plane had disintegrated in a violent explosion, spewing fingers of fire across the sky. Yeager, too, had given thought to how the end might come for him. He had awakened in the middle of many a night, in the throes of fantastic nightmares, most of which were associated with violent explosions, or the fear of being sealed inside the fiery bomb in a last plunge to earth.

The X-1 was wheeled out of the hangar and started on her way to the pit for fueling and mating to the B-29. Yeager sat in the cockpit, as he had done so many times before, rehearsing the procedures, which he had gone over and over endlessly. Upon his arrival at the pit the dedicated ground crew swung into action. Some of them began the fueling of the rocket plane, while other members of the team performed last-minute checks of various systems. The plane was then attached to the B-29.

The B-29 crew boarded the giant bomber, along with Yeager. Among them was Major Robert L. Cardenas, the pilot of the B-29, who was a veteran of X-plane delivery during early flights. Also on board was Major John Paul Stapp, the flight surgeon, who would go on to make notable contributions himself to the space and aeronautical world at a later date, when he would ride the rocket-propelled sleds to acquire medical data on how much a man can take in the way of high-gravity forces. And there was Captain Jackie L. Ridley, the engineer of the X-1 project, who was to supervise the drop.

The huge props turned on the black-and-silver bomber and she ambled out to a position at the end of the runway, to await takeoff instructions from the Edwards tower. Shortly after 10 A.M. the tower gave the mother ship's pilot the word to roll, and the lumbering veteran of the Pacific war and the skies over Japan moved down the runway.

As the B-29 droned slowly through 7,000 feet with her charge snuggled into the bomb bay, Captain Chuck Yeager left the B-29's crew compartment and made his way to the X-1's cockpit. There he made a final inspection of the orange bullet before sliding into her cockpit through the access hatch, located on the side and just in front of the leading edge of the right wing of the X-1. During the remaining climb of the two aircraft, he again rehearsed his flight plan for what he hoped would be a momentous achievement.

The pilot of the B-29 looked intently at the altimeter, which was coming up on 21,000 feet. Just as the needle arrived there, he retarded the throttles of the bomber and leveled off at a cruising speed of around 250 miles per hour.

The time for separation was close at hand, and Yeager began to check off items with the crew of the B-29. The word was given to

The X-1 falls from the belly of the B-29. Seconds later the rockets were ignited, and the little aircraft went on to write aeronautical history by breaking the sound barrier.

disconnect his oxygen hose from the mother ship and go on to the X-1 oxygen system. He also gave the signal to disconnect the nitrogen line which had been furnishing gas for the pressurization of the oxygen tank. The final item on his list was the jettison check, which was extremely vital because if he could not get rid of the fuel in short order, he would drop "like a streamlined anvil," in the vernacular of the test pilots, and he definitely could not land safely with a full load of the precarious fuel on board.

Just after Major Cardenas called out the two-minute drop warning, the Edwards tower broadcast a warning to all aircraft aloft to stay out of the area and for all aircraft on the ground to return to their parking positions.

Cardenas called out the one-minute count to Yeager, who braced himself in his seat. In hasty succession, the engineer gave last-minute instructions and indicated the potential trouble areas to which Yeager should be alerted. Then the monotonous count of the latter seconds began—10, 9, 8, 7, 6, 5, 4, 3, 2, 1. At 10:26 A.M., the shackle released the bright orange rocket ship and Chuck Yeager soared to possible doom, or a place of honor in aeronautical history.

Yeager floated weightlessly momentarily toward the top of the canopy. As he fell away from the B-29, the first words from him were "Firing four." While he spoke, the X-1 was moving rapidly out from under the bomber.

Yeager fired the number-two rocket chamber and the plane picked up additional momentum. He then cut off number four and

On January 5, 1949, Chuck Yeager took off in the X-1 from the dry lake bed at Edwards Air Force Base, another first for this uncanny little craft.

fired number three. After completing this sequence, he cut off number two and fired number one. He continued to fire the rocket chambers in various combinations and watched as the altimeter spun crazily on the instrument panel. At 35,000 feet, he continued to climb while the mach meter registered speeds no man had ever experienced before. Mach .92 was showing at this point on the instrument and he still raced aloft unchecked. He cut off number-three and number-one rocket chambers and coasted for a short interval, in order to grasp the situation which was unfolding at such a frantic pace. Glancing at the instruments, he was reassured that all was well. He then fired the number-three rocket chamber again. The mach meter jumped ahead to a reading of mach .96. He reported good acceleration and the fact that he was experiencing a mild buffeting. The controls, however, had responded very effectively, which again was reassuring. The mach meter suddenly fluctuated erratically, registered .98, and went off the scale. This was the great moment! Man, for the first time in history, had outdistanced the sound which his sophisticated machine of the air had generated as it passed through it. There was no wall, or any insurmountable barrier, after all, and the name of Chuck Yeager would be indelibly inscribed into the annals of aviation, along with the X-1.

This was not to be the end of experimenting for Captain Yeager with the X-1, however. In the remaining months of 1947 and on into 1948, he flew supersonic almost routinely. During these flights, he managed to pilot the stubborn bundle of lightning to an astounding 967 miles per hour. Another milestone was passed on January 5, 1949, when Yeager took off from the dry lake solely under the

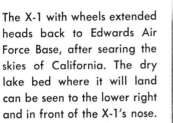

The X-1 with wheels extended heads back to Edwards Air Force Base, after searing the skies of California. The dry lake bed where it will land can be seen to the lower right and in front of the X-1's nose.

power of the X-1 and made a record climb to 23,000 feet in 100 seconds.

As Yeager's flights became more commonplace, other pilots checked out in the X-1. Lieutenant Colonel Frank Everest took a little bird to a record altitude in August 1949. On this date he reached 73,000 feet.

More advanced versions of the X-planes were built. First came the X-1A. The major difference between this newcomer and the X-1 was in her new turbo-driven rocket engine, in place of the pressurization from nitrogen gas employed on the first craft. Also, her dimensions were slightly larger. On the fourth flight in this improved bird, recently promoted Major Chuck Yeager blasted the air over California with a scorching 1,650 miles per hour. The following year, Major Arthur "Kit" Murray, a recently introduced pilot to the X program, rocketed to an altitude of more than 90,000 feet and aeronautical progress was on the brink of explosion!

The X-1, A through E, made vast contributions to aviation and space knowledge in rapid succession. Their pilots explored reaction controls, which were used most effectively at a later date by the Mercury, Gemini, and X-15 astronauts. These controls permit maneuvering in the airless environment of space and at the upper fringes of the atmosphere. Larger tanks were fitted to the rocket planes which boasted their range, speeds, and altitudes to an even greater extent.

The X-1 ran her soaring course, and ran it well. Yet, the X-1 was just another aeronautical plateau in man's never-ceasing desire to push back the frontiers of knowledge, no matter how formidable the barriers may seem to be.

8

The Thermal Thicket

While the X-1 was making rapid strides in pushing back the aeronautical frontier, another aircraft was being readied to vie for the laurels of pushing it back even further.

The U.S. Navy was equally interested in exploring the new flight regimes of the sonic barrier—and any other aeronautical barriers which might lie ahead. Navy representatives met with the experts of NACA (National Advisory Committee for Aeronautics) redesignated NASA in 1958, to spell out their specifications for such an aircraft. Unlike its Air Force counterpart, the Navy's Skyrocket, as she was aptly labeled, would feature a combination power plant with a conventional jet engine, as well as a rocket engine. The Navy's plan was to utilize the jet engine for takeoff and the climb to altitude. Realizing the major shortcomings of the rocket engine in its voracious appetite for fuel, the designers figured that by using a jet engine for the takeoff and climb to altitude, the rocket engine would retain many more precious seconds of fuel with which to explore certain unsolved flight dimensions, such as tremendously increased speeds and altitudes which only the rocket-powered craft was capable of attaining. Actually, three in this series were built. However, the first two, designated Skystreak I's, were powered

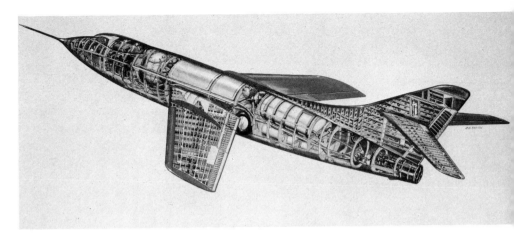

This phantom view of the Douglas Skyrocket shows the general layout of the tankage and its Reaction Motors XLR-8 powerplant. She recorded many laurels in a fast-growing log of achievements.

by jet engines only. They gave a very creditable account of themselves, however, by topping several speed and altitude records for jet aircraft. Misfortune struck the program on May 3, 1948, when Howard Lilly, a NACA test pilot, was killed on takeoff in one of the Skyrocket I's.

The rocket-jet equipped Skyrocket was flown for the first time in February 1948. The aircraft took off from Edwards dry lake with her own primary power plant. From that day forward to the end of 1948 the Skyrocket had been piloted to speeds beyond that of sound on many occasions.

The urgency for further advancing aeronautical research became much more pronounced when the United States entered the Korean conflict. As a result, higher priorities were given to almost all programs devoted to greater aerial achievement.

The Skyrocket would record additional laurels in her fast-growing log of achievements. On June 11, 1951, Douglas test pilot Bill Bridgeman flew the Skyrocket to an unofficial speed and altitude record of more than 1,200 miles per hour and 70,000 feet, respectively. Before the year was ended he would break his own records in rapid succession by piloting the sleek bullet-shaped craft to a speed of 1,238 miles per hour and to an altitude of more than 79,000 feet.

The D-558 Skyrocket hybrid aircraft equipped with both jet and rocket engines takes off from Edwards Air Force Base, California. This aircraft was the first in aviation history to fly at twice the speed of sound.

In the course of striving for greater speeds and higher altitudes, the Skyrocket engineers deduced that in order to attain the absolute maximum they would have to adopt the techniques used so effectively in the X-1 program, i.e., the air drop from the mother aircraft. They also decided to remove the jet engine from the Skyrocket. In the space formerly occupied by the jet power plant would be placed tanks with which to accommodate more fuel. This would, in turn, give the perky little craft's rocket engine, the XLR-8, extra seconds of burning time. This engine was also built by Reaction Motors, the firm that had done such a notable job in producing the power plant for the X-1. This would prove to be all important in driving the Skyrocket to her maximum design limits. The modification proved its worth in the ensuing year, when NACA test pilot Scott Crossfield rocketed to a speed of more than 1,328 miles per hour, becoming the first man in history to top the "twice the speed of sound" barrier.

While Scott Crossfield was increasing the speed record, Lieutenant Colonel Marion Carl was taking care of the altitude records.

On August 21, 1953, he rocketed to more than 83,000 feet above Edwards Air Force Base. Both these records were set while using the B-29 drop technique which effectively demonstrated the wisdom of the plan to remove the jet power plant.

With the records tumbling so rapidly at Edwards, a friendly rivalry developed between the Navy's Skyrocket team and the Air Force X-1 group. Major Chuck Yeager, not content to see the speed record held by the Navy for a lengthy period, flew the modified X-1 to a speed of more than 1,612 miles per hour, to best Scott Crossfield's record by some 300 miles per hour. Reaction Motors had made major changes in the fuel-pumping mechanism of this super-rocket engine which permitted Yeager to fly at these phenomenal speeds.

An interesting aspect of the relationship of a test pilot to his aircraft is the fact that, as he becomes more familiar with it—and this he must do—a strong affinity develops which comes to light in the way he addresses certain references to its performance or its description. For instance, if the bird performs well on a given flight, he will most likely refer to it as "she" or "her," just as sailors do when speaking of their ships. On the other hand, if the aircraft performs badly, the pilot might talk disparagingly of "it" or even

The sleek Skyrocket II nestled in the bomb bay of the B-29 mother aircraft from which it was dropped for speed and altitude runs.

"the beast." The terms are used alternately but, in the main, they connote intense affection for the craft.

With the Soviet built MIGs threatening the aerial supremacy of the United States in the skies over Korea, thoughts now were turned to the very practical application of rocket engines in fighter aircraft. An attempt to develop such a fighter for use as an exceptionally fast interceptor was unfolding at the Flight Test Center at Edwards Air Force Base. This aircraft was designated the XF-91 and was built by Republic Aircraft Corporation. Like the Skyrocket, it was fitted with both jet and rocket engines. Again, Reaction Motors was selected to build the rocket power plant. It was designed to give the fighter the capability to put on a tremendous burst of speed in order to overtake any potential adversary.

Not only was this skill in the sky particularly desirable in light of the tense feelings between the United States and the Soviet Union because of Korea, it was now a pressing urgency for the Soviets had triggered their first nuclear devices. Inevitably, much thought was given at the highest level of government in the United States as to the ability of the Soviets to deliver nuclear weapons to the continent of North America. The development of a fighter to intercept such bombers with such awesome payloads was given top priority.

The XF-91 flew supersonically for the first time during the month of December 1952. Although its concept and design appeared sound at the start, continued tests, in addition to breakthroughs in conventional jet-powered fighters, proved that it was not effective enough as a standard interceptor. However, much basic knowledge was derived from the endeavor and in the final analysis, this is the reason for the X-plane series. As was the case with the Skyrocket and the X-1. Collectively, this trio pushed back several aeronautical barriers to the absolute limits of their structure. These limitations made them incapable of soaring on to the conquest of the next obstacle—the thermal barrier.

In the final days of the X-1 program, and as other experimental aircraft continued to expand the speed and altitude parameters, the talk among pilots and engineers began to pivot almost entirely

One of the first efforts to blend the characteristics of the jet engine and the rocket engines into a fast interceptor was demonstrated in the XF-91 shown above. The Reaction Motors-built rocket unit is mounted in the protrusion below the fuselage.

around yet another barrier. They resisted calling it a barrier. However, probably because of the overexposure of the word throughout the pioneering days of the X-1, they chose, instead, to call it the THERMAL THICKET. The first of the X-planes, and the Skyrocket, had nudged the fringes of this new barrier, as had the propeller-driven planes and German jet and rocket planes of World War II. There were newly aroused inclinations throughout aviation circles to divert much of future research activities in this direction.

Although the limitations of their power plants alone would have prevented the X-1 and the Skyrocket from penetrating the thermal barrier, they would not have been able to survive even if they could have surmounted this plateau. Their soft aluminum wings and fuselages would have melted had they been pushed into the realm of the heat thicket, plunging their pilots to certain doom.

The thermal barrier, or thermal thicket, whichever you prefer, is experienced when an aircraft attains a speed of around 2,000 miles per hour. At such speeds the temperatures on the wings and fuselage soar to readings of more than 500 degrees Fahrenheit, enough to melt aluminum or other soft metals, as stated above.

To investigate this new dimension of flight, the Air Force and the National Advisory Committee for Aeronautics contracted with Bell Aircraft Corporation to build an airplane capable of exploring this recently discovered hindrance to man's progress in aviation.

The specifications were much more exacting than those required in the X-1. For instance, the skin of her wings would be made of stainless steel and the fuselage of K-monel metal—an alloy of copper and nickel.

This airplane, in keeping with the system of designating aircraft built exclusively for research purposes, was simply called X-2, meaning she would be the second of the new series.

Two of the novel features built into this bird would be the sweep of her wings and the increased power and greater sophistication of her rocket engine. Instead of an engine that operated at the same thrust levels while firing, the X-2's engine would be throttable. This was quite novel in contrast to the system used on the X-1, in which the only control over thrust output involved the selection of one or more of the individual rocket chambers, which could be used in various combinations.

Since the X-2 would be heavier than her predecessor, the X-1, a more versatile airplane was required to lift her to altitude for drop. The four-engine B-50 bomber, which was selected for the chore, could be considered the first stage booster, when speaking in terms of modern-day space launching for, in essence, this was exactly the role it played.

Another unique feature of the X-2, in contrast to her X-1 predecessor, was the landing gear. Instead of the usual wheels, she was

The X-2 being mated to the B-50 mother ship. The B-50 served in effect as a first-stage booster. By lifting the little rocket airplane to altitude, more fuel remained for propelling the craft to its design limits.

equipped with a single nose wheel and two metal skids, similar to skis, in place of the rear wheels which were to be found on the X-1. These were to serve a dual purpose. They would slow down the aircraft rapidly on touchdown for a landing and they would be much less complex as well as lighter in construction. Weight is always an important factor to consider in rocket aircraft where fuel for longer bursts of power was considered to be at such a premium.

The Bell Aircraft Corporation, manufacturer of the new airplane, selected Skip Ziegler as the company's pilot for the initial tests, which would consist of drops from the B-50 bomber to check the stability and control of the X-2 without power. He had also gained earlier rocket experience in the X-1. He maneuvered the X-2 in order to get the feel of the controls and the airplane in general, then headed for a landing on the dry lake bed at Edwards Air Force Base in California. Upon touchdown at very high speed, the X-2 veered sharply to the right, with the pilot in trouble and the airplane in obvious jeopardy. The nose wheel collapsed during the wild ride that followed, causing one of the craft's wing tips to dig into the sand. The airplane spun completely around and came to an abrupt halt.

As a result of this incident, the engineers decided to add two additional small skids, one on either side, farther out toward the wing tips. These would serve to keep the aircraft from tipping over on making contact with the ground. After the modification was completed, Ziegler flew the rocket plane for a second time. The glide back and the landing were accomplished without any trouble.

For the third flight, Air Force Major Frank "Pete" Everest, who had been selected as the test pilot for the X-2 project, was invited to fly this revolutionary new aircraft. On Everest's flight, the drop and subsequent flight back to the lake bed went well. However, trouble cropped up. As he was about to drop the shiny bullet on to the runway, he received an instrument indication that the left main skid had failed to extend. This sent a momentary chill up Everest's spine but, as is so characteristic of test pilots, he remained cool and braced for the wild gyrations which would surely follow. He had no alternative but to ride it out. There could be no go-arounds for another chance at landing, or an opportunity to circle the pattern in order to study the situation. Just as Everest felt for the ground with control stick, the right skid made impact. It jarred the left skid down from its recessed housing.

With these three glide tests out of the way, the airplane was sent back to Buffalo, New York, to the Bell Aircraft Corporation for installation of the rocket engine.

Many efforts were made to change the fuel flow system and the tankage in the X-2, in order to make it safe for flight. The engineers remembered all too vividly the explosions which had occurred with later versions of the X-1. But all of their precautions proved to be in vain, for on a captive flight of the X-2 over Lake Ontario a fire and explosion rocked the bomb bay of the mother B-50 bomber which was carrying the precarious cargo. Skip Ziegler, one of America's great test pilots, was engulfed in the inferno as he stood in the bomb bay beside the X-2 checking the cockpit prior to entry. Frank Wolko, an assistant to Ziegler, was also killed in the explosion.

This incident cast an air of gloom over the X-2 project and set the program back more than a year while engineers attempted to decipher what had gone wrong. The fact that they had to wait for the completion of a second X-2 before test flights could be resumed set the schedule back even further.

In the summer of 1954, the second X-2 was delivered to Edwards Air Force Base in the belly of a B-50 mother airplane, for resumption of test flights. Prior to arrival, it was decided that Major Everest would be the primary pilot for the project. He was particularly eager to get on with the program.

The engine had not yet been installed in the second X-2 and the flights which Everest would conduct initially would also be mere gliding flights back to the base, so that he might acquire a complete feel for the airplane and its handling characteristics.

In the ensuing days, Everest experienced incidents similar to the one which Skip Ziegler had undergone earlier. On one of the flights one of the whisker skids which had been installed to keep the airplane from veering over on to the right or the left wing tip failed to come down prior to landing. Upon contact with the ground, the

X-2 bolted off on a tangent and careened out of control across the barren lake bed. Everest was helpless to do anything but sit there and ride until it stopped. After turning a full ninety degrees, it finally wound up spinning completely around and skidding backward until its momentum had been spent.

Although the damage which the airplane incurred was not major in nature, it was sufficient to require that it be taken back to the Bell plant in Buffalo for repairs. While the repairs were in progress, a decision was made to install the rocket engine at the same time. This was considered important, for the program was running considerably behind schedule and there were many people who had begun to look askance at the whole project in light of the discouraging problems which had been encountered. Further difficulties with the engine installation forced the group to return the airplane to Edwards for additional glide tests. These were intended to solve the landing-gear problem which, at this point, still had to be overcome before the experimenters could risk powered flights.

Back at Edwards, Everest took the sleek little dart up for more powerless glides back to the lake. Again he experienced the uncontrollable gyrations across the lake on landing. These happened with such great frequency that at one point the intrepid test pilot almost considered quitting the project. Everest's criticism of the landing problem was so emphatic that the craft was returned to Buffalo for further work on the gear. After a hastily-called huddle of engineers, a decision was made to cut the height of the landing gear in half in order to get the airplane closer to the ground, lowering its center of gravity and thus giving it greater stability upon landing. The nose wheel was also modified by curtailing the castering limits (the ability to move left and right), so that it would be in reasonably true alignment with the direction in which the airplane would be traveling upon landing. The gear modifications were completed along with the installation of the engine and the X-2 was again lugged back across the continent to Edwards in the belly of the B-50 bomber. There the flights were hastily scheduled, for time was running out for the X-2 project. The deadline to which it had been committed was drawing uncomfortably near.

Everest made additional glide flights to confirm to himself—and to the Bell engineers—that the landing-gear problems had been solved. With the exception of a few minor incidents, they went off well.

On November 18, 1955, the X-2 was hoisted aboard the B-50 mother aircraft and carried to altitude high in the California skies, where she was dropped. For the first time in the X-2's rather chaotic history she would move out from under the bomber under her own power. The small aircraft dropped away from the giant bomber much more abruptly than had been the case when she was dropped with ballast alone. But, unperturbed by the unexpected, Pete Everest started the rocket engine and prepared for all that would lie ahead. As the test pilot moved the throttle forward, the little beast bolted off into the blue, the air-speed indicator spinning furiously toward the speed of sound. When it registered about eight-tenths of its objective, Major Stu Childs, who was following Major Everest in an F-100 fighter chase airplane, moved in close to look over the X-2. This is routine procedure for a test flight. As he moved under the rocket plane, he noticed that the horizontal stabilizer was buffeting erratically. He immediately notified Everest of this problem. The test pilot quickly cut his engine and decreased the speed to see if the buffeting would stop. It did, and after a short interval of coasting flight he restarted the rocket engine and was once more on his way. Major Childs again reported the buffeting. The intrepid X-2 pilot cut his engine once more to see if the problem could be overcome. He again moved the throttle forward to restart the engine. After a brief spurt, the engine coughed and stopped abruptly. Realizing the hazards of trying to land with fuel on board, Everest began to jettison the vehicle's fuel while heading for home.

Safely back on the ground at Edwards, an inspection of the X-2 revealed that there had been a fire in the rocket-engine compartment. Had the small inferno raged a few additional seconds, the aircraft—and possibly Everest—might have been blown to oblivion.

One day, while repairs were being made on the X-2, a modified version of the X-1 was being flown over California on one of its several follow-up flights to acquire additional rocket-plane knowledge. It exploded prior to its release from the mother plane. Fortunately, no one was killed or injured in the incident, However, this disaster did have such a resounding impact on officials at the Flight Test Center that the X-2 was grounded while modifications were being made in her tankage and propellant system which, after investigation, had been confirmed as the source of trouble in the exploding X-1. This occurrence delayed the program several more months, much to the consternation of Major Everest and the rest of the test crew.

On March 26, 1956, Everest was given the green light to start flying again. On this occasion he pushed the renovated X-2 to a speed of around mach .91, or 91 per cent of the speed of sound. This was nothing to startle the aeronautical world, for that speed had been exceeded many times already by the X-1. Everest was merely nudging the aircraft forward in very orderly increments, because this was to be the mode of operation for the tests—feel one's way gradually, hoping to nip any potential hazards in the bud before they could reach destructive proportions. On April 25, Everest pushed the X-2 beyond the barrier and then again on May 1. These and additional flights reassured Everest that the second of the X-planes was stable and durable enough to go all out—that is, all out insofar as her rocket engine and the limited fuel supply would permit.

The X-2, designed to conquer the thermal barrier encountered in the vicinity of 2000 miles per hour. The heat generated on the skin of an aircraft traveling at this speed frequently soars to temperatures in excess of 500 degrees.

The ninth flight of the X-2 was intended to explore the so-called thermal thicket and the stability characteristics of the aircraft at such speeds. In rehearsing for all of these flights, Everest flew simulated missions in an electronic trainer. These were intended to acquaint him with potential problems that he might encounter. During these mock missions he discovered that various combinations of circumstances would cause the airplane to go out of control. This alerted the test pilot to the fact that such things could occur and that he should be on the watch for them during his upcoming flights.

The lumbering bomber arrived at the prescribed altitude in midmorning. The X-2, with Everest at the controls, was released. He fell earthward briefly, almost vertically, until his gloved hand pushed forward on the throttle. The rocket engine spewed flaming power equivalent to 100,000 horses, pushed the minute white lightning bolt through the blue California sky at an unbelievable speed. The fantastic acceleration that Everest experienced jammed him into his seat as no pilot had ever before been compressed by acceleration alone. The instrument readings lagged behind the actual speeds and altitudes through which he was moving, for they could not keep up. Multicolored stripes which had been painted on the nose of the aircraft, in order to permit the engineers to compute the temperatures that would be experienced on the airplane's skin, began to burn and peel off. The paint was of a special texture and very carefully prepared for use in this experiment. This debris, flying off the fuselage, pelted Everest's windshield. There was no doubt about it —he was in the midst of the dreaded thermal barrier and, so far, it had been conquered without ill effects.

The flight continued with incredible ease. A modification of the fueling system had permitted the X-2's powerful engine to burn for four additional seconds, which seems minute in terms of time. However, it was sufficient to hurl the manned projectile through space at a speed never before experienced by man. When the speed of sound indicator finally caught up with the actual speed of the airplane, it registered an astounding 1,900 miles per hour.

After decelerating somewhat, Everest did a few additional turning maneuvers to slow down the X-2, as he also prepared for his

Lt/Col. Frank (Pete) Everest, shown in the cockpit of the X-2 in which he set so many speed and altitude records. His flights also paved the way for the conquest of the thermal barrier.

return to the base. When his now powerless airplane descended to a lower altitude, he was met by the accompanying chase pilots, making their rendezvous at the prearranged point called for in the flight plan. Everest was so exuberant about the results of the flight that he even did a few victory rolls to convey to them word of his success. He was bound by security to maintain radio silence. The only word he was permitted to say was "bingo," a code word known only to the crews on the ground and in the air who were monitoring the flight.

As the X-2 skidded to a landing on the dry lake in the usual accompanying cloud of dust, the ground crew converged on the airplane and its pilot, to congratulate him on the success of the mission. Handshakes and back slaps were in abundance as they pulled Pete Everest from the cockpit. This was to be Everest's last flight in the X-2, but it was a flight which would be indelibly written into the annals of aviation and one which would inscribe his name as a pioneer whose flights would ultimately lead to the crossing of the thermal barrier.

Two youthful engineer pilots—Captain Iven Kincheloe and Captain Milburn Apt—had been understudying the newly promoted Colonel Everest as he put the X-2 through her initial paces. They represented the first of a new breed in experimental aviation engineering test pilots who could not only put the aircraft through the required paces, but who could also converse as engineers with the engineers who designed and built the exotic test airplanes. The X-planes were becoming so complex that the pilots who flew them had to be able to understand their innermost nature and exactly what they were intended to do. Gone were the stick-and-rudder pilots of yesteryear.

Captain Iven Kincheloe was picked for the next test in the X-2, which would send the manned bullet on a maximum altitude flight. Kincheloe was a jet ace of the Korean War and he was extremely eager to pit his skill against the unknown which the X-2 was designed to explore.

On September 7, 1956, Captain Kincheloe was given his opportunity, and he piloted the X-2 to an altitude of more than 126,000 feet, higher than any other human had ever gone. This flight could be considered a milestone, even without the contributions it had made to aeronautics. For it might truthfully be said that Captain Iven Kincheloe was the first man to penetrate the boundaries of space, for after leaving 100,000 feet, his craft was a ballistic missile, hurtling along through the void without aerodynamic support. His craft actually would not fly again until he returned to that part of the atmosphere which would be sufficient to support it as an aircraft, rather than as the space craft it had just been.

The plan for the X-2 through the remainder of her tests would be to alternate pilots and the missions for the miniature flying laboratory. For the next mission, a decision was made to send the X-2 on a flight to acquire data on speeds even higher than those experienced by Colonel Everest. Captain Milburn Apt was designated as the pilot for this flight. Apt had flown one of the chase planes on several other X-2 flights, and he had checked out in the simulator, so he was well acquainted with the potential pitfalls of the experimental airplane. His engineering mind had already calculated how he would coax the maximum speed out of the airplane by prolonging the burning time of the rocket.

On September 27, Apt was dropped from the belly of the B-50 bomber to begin his run through the brilliantly clear California sky. This was the thirteenth powered flight of the X-2 and Apt not prone to superstition hoped that it would be the most significant one.

Prior to the drop, all fifty-one of the items on his check list had checked out properly and he ignited the rocket engine. It emitted a booming roar. Kincheloe was flying chase for Apt and he stayed with him until he reached about 50,000 feet. At this point, Apt had begun to leave the supersonic jet fighter which Kincheloe was flying far behind. He even set a new world record while climbing, and in his methodical way managed to squeeze six additional seconds of burning time out of the powerful rocket engine. The engine at this point in time was producing power sufficient to propel an aircraft carrier. The airspeed indicator was spinning wildly as the X-2 pierced the sky like a runaway bullet. When the mach meter registered 3.2 (2,178 miles per hour), Apt sent word that he was turning. Except for an eerie screeching sound over the radio, those would be the last words ever uttered by this courageous test pilot. The X-2 rolled violently out of control and experienced what the aeronautical engineers call inertial coupling, which simply means that the airplane was spinning on all three axes at once.

Apt fought valiantly to save himself and the X-2 from destruction, as motion pictures taken over his shoulder later confirmed. He was thrashed violently around the cockpit and evidently slammed into unconsciousness against the canopy as he plummeted earthward, for his helmet could be seen to bounce violently off the sides of the cockpit. At 40,000 feet he regained consciousness briefly and tried to save the airplane from an inevitable plunge to earth. But, sensing that his efforts were all in vain, he hit the ejection switch, which would sever the nose section of the aircraft from the main part of the fuselage. He was again knocked unconscious. Somehow—probably subconsciously—he readied himself for bail out from the nose capsule. He unhooked his seat belt and his shoulder harness and armed the device which would have blown the canopy for him to bail out with his personal parachute. However, by the time he had gone through these procedures, he must have lapsed into unconsciousness again, for he did not get over the side of the capsule. It struck the ground at a terrific speed, carrying this bold pilot to his death.

With the unhappy death of Captain Apt came the end of the X-2 program, a program which had gathered invaluable informa-

Captain Ivan Kincheloe (left) who flew the X-2 to its highest altitude mark, and Captain Milburn Apt (right), who flew the little bundle of lightning to the highest speed mark of its remarkable career. Captain Apt was killed when the X-2 went wildly out of control in the process of attaining a speed of 2,064 miles an hour. Captain Kincheloe, who was selected to fly the X-15, was killed later in a fighter on takeoff from Edwards Air Force Base in a routine flight.

tion and had exerted a profound impact on United States leadership in the field of aeronautics. These contributions to aviation can be seen on every hand today, as in the swept-wing fighters and transports which traverse the skies of the world. Also, the new metals which will be used on the supersonic transports—and the supersonic transport itself—will have benefited by the flights of Captain Iven Kincheloe, Captain Apt, and Colonel Pete Everest.

Ironically, a few days after Apt's fatal flight, Captain Kincheloe took off in an F-104 to simulate flights in a more advanced rocket-plane. At the end of an Edwards Air Force Base runway the fighter's engine flamed out. The aircraft was equipped with an ejection seat which propelled the escaping pilot downward, rather than upward, as most escape seats do. Thinking nimbly, as he had always done so ably previously, Kincheloe flipped the little fighter upside down in an effort to eject upward. His fight for life was all in vain, unfortunately. He was killed after falling to earth in a half-opened parachute.

9

The X-15 and the
Space Barrier

The X-15 project was conceived in the summer of 1952, when the NACA, now NASA, assigned to its laboratories the task of studying the higher speeds associated with flight. Initially, most of the engineers thought the research might be conducted with the use of models which could be put through their paces in the giant wind tunnels operated at the various research facilities. After two years of debating the subject, a recommendation was made to the U.S. Air Force and Navy to consider the building of an aircraft that would be capable of attaining speeds in excess of 4,000 miles per hour and of reaching altitudes in excess of 250,000 feet (approximately forty-eight miles).

In July 1954 representatives of the Air Force, Navy, and NACA met to consider this proposal, which was accepted unanimously. Shortly thereafter, contractors were invited to bid on the construction of such an aircraft. In the fall of 1955, North American Aviation was selected to build the airplane. Bids were also solicited for the design and building of an engine capable of hurling the new craft, which now had been given the designation of X-15, through the skies at 4,000 miles per hour, thrusting her out of the atmosphere and into the environment of space. In September 1956, Reaction Motors, a division of Thiokol Chemical Corporation, which had had such great success in building earlier engines for the X-1, the XF-91, and the Skyrocket, was commissioned to build such an engine—which was given the designation of XLR-99.

To support the X-15 flight, which would take place out of Edwards Air Force Base—as had the flights of her predecessors, the X-1 and X-2—construction of a series of lengthy tracking stations was approved. This was necessary because the X-15 could go so much farther and faster in such a short time than her rocket ancestors ever did. The new tracking system would be known as the high range and the facility would extend from Wendover, Utah, to Edwards Air Force Base, California. The route along which these stations would be positioned for tracking was selected for several reasons, but, most importantly, the choice was because of the natural dry-lake landing strips which are located along that stretch of territory. This area is also sparsely populated, which would minimize the number of people who might be disturbed by the sonic booms that the X-15 would generate behind her as she slammed through the atmospheric sea of molecules.

To serve as the first stage booster for the X-15, two B-52 eight-jet bombers were modified to serve as drop aircraft for the three hybrid crafts which were about to be introduced to the astro and aeronautical world.

In early 1958, just prior to delivery of the first X-15, it became apparent that the XLR rocket engine would be delayed somewhat because of the complex nature of its development. Anticipating the possibility of such setbacks, the program managers had already decided to avoid holding up the first flights by installing two old X-1 engines in one of the X-15's. By doing this, they could begin shaking down the new rocket craft immediately to try to detect any unexpected design problems she might exhibit. The two engines which were to be mounted one above the other would give the newest of the X-planes more than 16,000 pounds of thrust.

The major task for this unusual bird is to gather data, and her ability in this field of activity considerably outdistances that of her

Rocket sled test of the X-15 ejection seat. Stabilization of the seat is brought about by use of the striped control surfaces shown to the left and right of the test subject.

cousins which flew before her. For instance, the X-15 can gather more scientific information on one flight than the X-1 could gather on thirty. The X-2 was equipped with fifteen temperature sensors at various spots on her wings and fuselage. She had no pressure-sensing devices and only 550 total pounds of instrumentation. The X-15 has more than 1,300 pounds of sensing gear, which includes 600 temperature-sensing points and 140 other sensors recording pressures across her wings and body. Sensing the physical condition of her pilot at the speeds and altitudes to which he flies is also one of the tasks she performs. Such data proved extremely important to the astronauts of the Mercury program and assisted greatly in the planning of the first manned space flights.

The escape system of the X-15 differs from that of the X-2 in that the pilot is ejected just as he would be from a disabled high-performance fighter aircraft. But because of the tremendous speed at which the X-15 pilot might be forced to eject, great precautions have been taken to afford him a chance to survive. One of the potential problems of high-speed escape was confirmed in rocket sled runs which demonstrated the violent tumbling actions that might befall the pilot. To counter this hazard, two winglike control surfaces were designed to spring out from the sides of the X-15's ejection seat. This device would serve to stabilize the latter, causing the chair and the escaping pilot in it to fly a relatively smooth trajectory upon leaving the aircraft. One aspect of escape related to the space missions which the X-15 pilots fly, and one lesson to which the X-15 pilots have learned to pay rapt attention is the briefing regarding possible bail out and surest methods for survival which they are given as a preliminary to one of the maximum altitude runs.

If a pilot has occasion to eject on the way up, as the X-15 leaps out of the atmosphere at several thousand miles per hour, he must, even under the most dire circumstances, resist the impulse to do so. If he did, his body would travel along a trajectory identical to that of the airplane. His path would resemble that of a ballistic missile, and he would plunge back into the atmosphere in identical fashion. Probably he would spin wildly as he returned, for there would be insufficient air to enable the stabilizing fins of the seat to gain control in order to keep him on an even keel. In addition, the frictional heat generated on his body, and his space suit would be sufficient to turn him into a human torch almost instantaneously.

Although one of the X-15's predecessors, the X-1, was equipped for maneuvering in a spacelike environment with reaction jets, her basic power plant was not capable of propelling her sufficiently far enough into space really to give the pilot an opportunity to use these controls effectively. To the X-15 pilot these reaction jets were absolute musts, for at the speeds and altitudes to which he would be flying re-entry into the earth's atmosphere would be extremely critical, even with these controls. Without them, the craft would enter in the same attitude in which it was positioned in departing from the atmosphere. In most cases this meant that the tail would make contact with the atmosphere first, creating a precarious control problem and most likely resulting in a loss of control of the craft upon entry, in addition to the violent G-forces brought to bear on the pilot during such an experience. With the reaction controls, the pilot would be able to position the X-15 for a proper re-entry attitude by placing the nose down and the tail up.

On March 10, 1959, the first of the X-15's to be delivered was taken aloft under the wing of the B-52 for her first shakedown flight. On this occasion she would not be dropped, but would merely be put through a check of it's many complex systems, to determine how they would perform at altitude. The engineers and the pilot would also get some indication of her flight characteristics during this tryout, even though she would be rigidly attached to the B-52. Three additional captive flights were made in April and May, to acquire more extensive data.

With North American test pilot Scott Crossfield at the controls, the X-15 was dropped for her first free flight on June 8, 1959. The flight was without power and lasted a scant five minutes while he glided the eerie black craft back to the dry lake at Edwards Air Force Base. With free-flight success behind them, the engineers decided to give Crossfield the green light for the first powered flight. On September 17, 1959, the X-15, equipped with two X-1 engines, was flown to an altitude of more than 52,000 feet at a speed of nearly 1,400 miles per hour. All went well and the data she acquired and the experience her pilot obtained concerning her handling characteristics now began to expand.

Crossfield encountered trouble on the third powered flight of the rocket craft, however, when an explosion shook the X-15 just after launching, at an altitude of around 44,000 feet. Crossfield calmly shut down the rocket chambers and began to jettison the fuel. This was most important, for to retain the fuel on board was not only precarious, but the weight of it upon touching down could change the center of gravity of the airplane, thus changing its gliding characteristics drastically for landing. Crossfield also decided to use an alternate landing field, which was handier—Rosamond dry lake. This is also a part of the sprawling Edwards Air Force Base complex. Things were going well for this calm and very skillful pilot and he thought the landing would be a normal one. However, in the last moments, just prior to touchdown, another gremlin appeared. The nose wheel collapsed on impact with the lake bed. The contact was so violent that the rocket plane broke in two just behind the cockpit. Miraculously, Crossfield was unhurt as the smashed X-15

Cutaway shows the general layout of the X-15 equipped with the large power plant, the XLR-99. Fuel tanks are mounted in front of the engine.

skidded to an abrupt halt.

The badly-damaged aircraft was returned to the North American plant in Los Angeles where it was repaired and rescheduled to fly within a ninety-day period. The tempo of flights increased in the first part of 1960 and confidence in the pilot's ability to handle this hybrid new craft continued to mount simultaneously. After several more flights by Crossfield, the X-15 was turned over to the Air Force and NASA.

NASA's chief pilot, Joe Walker, one of the world's greatest test pilots, was selected to make the first flight for the government. On March 25, 1960, Walker went aloft under the wing of the carrier B-52 bomber and was dropped. This flight was planned merely to give him a feel for the controls of this revolutionary new craft. He put the bird briefly through its paces, but very conservatively, attaining an altitude of only 48,000 feet and a speed of mach 2—an altitude and speed which he had experienced many times in much less sophisticated airplanes.

The number-three X-15 was delivered to Edwards in the spring of 1960 and the project engineers began to put the craft through a series of grueling ground checks before it could take to the air. This was particularly important, for she was equipped with the huge

XLR-99 engine, a new power plant built by Reaction Motors, pioneers of the famous X-1 engine. On June 8, 1960, as the engine was being run up on a ground test, misfortune struck. A pressure regulator failed to operate properly, which caused overpressurization of the fuel tank. The ensuing explosion blew the X-15 apart. The battered remnants of the craft were refurbished and reassembled. Meanwhile, Joe Walker and newly-introduced Air Force Major Bob White alternated in making flights in the number-one X-15 aircraft, to gain experience and to acquire performance data. During this period the number-two aircraft was also fitted with the big XLR-99 engine and made ready for flight.

Prompted by the near-fatal accident that had happened to the number-three aircraft, more extensive ground checks were conducted on number two. Fulfilling North American's contractual obligations, Scott Crossfield returned to demonstrate to the Air Force and to NASA the air worthiness of this versatile rocket craft when flown with the enormous power generated by the XLR-99 engine. This awesome power is equivalent to that of seven Navy cruisers—one-half million horsepower. It is also sufficient to hurl a man and his sleek machine out of the earth's atmosphere into the hostile environment of space. One of the major and more desirable features of this new power source was the fact that it was throttlable —that is the ability of the pilot to parcel out very precise increments of power for a variety of missions.

On November 15, 1960, Crossfield unleashed the power of the new engine and attained a speed of just under three times the velocity of sound. In describing the power of the new engine after the flight, the pilot said that merely cutting the power from the engine was "about like hitting a stone wall with a truck." This description is very apt, for the power of the XLR-99 engine is also roughly equivalent to the final stage of the Atlas booster which placed our Mercury astronauts in orbit. Relating the flights of the X-15 to the flights of the Mercury astronauts is not far afield, for there were many project people in the early stages of planning the X-15 who advocated orbital flights, or near-orbital flights, for the sleek black bird.

The X-15, above, tucked under the wing of the B-52 mother aircraft, heads out for another exploratory mission. It is released, left, after passing through the denser regions of the atmosphere, a distinct advantage in gathering valuable basic data for use by aeronautical and astronautical engineers in designing futuristic aircraft and spacecraft.

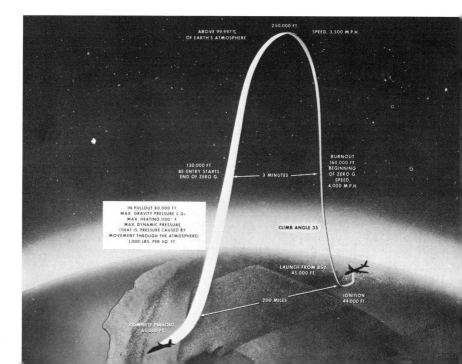

The testing of the X-15 was to proceed on a very orderly basis, pushing back the barriers in small increments. And push them back they did. Additional pilots joined the team, and they have also written their names indelibly into the aeronautical record books. Neil Armstrong, who has subsequently flown as a Gemini astronaut, piloted the X-15 on numerous significant ventures which probed the unknowns of aeronautical and space sciences. Many people credit Armstrong's cool handling of the wildly spinning Gemini when it was thrown out of control by a stuck thruster to his experience in the X-15 program. This was the greatest hazard encountered in the entire Gemini program and it was brought under control in a most skillful way.

Realizing how critical the re-entry maneuver was to safe penetration of the atmosphere, X-15 engineers invented an instrument called the Q-Ball. This device affords the pilot an indication of the angle at which he is re-entering. This is vital information for the successful completion of a mission. If the pilot re-enters too steeply, he could overstress the airplane, leading to possible disintegration. On the other hand, too shallow a re-entry could sustain the heat for a prolonged period, thus weakening the metals, possibly leading to catastrophe. Neil Armstrong flew the first flight with the Q-Ball-equipped airplane on December 9, 1960.

From this point on the flights picked up in tempo, although varied in purpose.

Tragedy struck the X-15 program on November 15, 1967, during a flight which involved the flight testing of a revolutionary ramjet engine which was attached externally to the X-15's fuselage. The ramjet was a part of a rather extensive Air Force research and development program to explore the use of ramjet engines in futuristic aerospacecraft. Major Michael J. Adams, the Air Force test pilot for the flight, was killed as the X-15 disintegrated at an altitude of between 60,000 and 70,000 feet, as he was climbing out after leaving the B-52 carrier plane, to make a run with the engine to explore its power potential and the aerodynamic effects of its shape in the

Diagram, left, shows a typical flight profile for the X-15. Altitudes in excess of that shown have been attained on many occasions.

The typical team required to see a successful X-15 flight to completion. The smaller aircraft (upper left) are chase planes, usually flown by other X-15 pilots to observe externally how the mission is going and to report any unusual events to the pilot and to the ground stations. The B-52 mother ship is making a low pass over the X-15 in salute to a successful mission.

Not all flights of the X-15 ended in complete success. The photo below shows the aftermath of a flight by test pilot John McKay. The nose wheel collapsed on landing, causing the craft to skid nose down across the dry lake bed. After skidding for a considerable distance it swerved, then rolled completely over on its back. McKay sustained only minor injuries.

The X-15 is expected to attain speeds of over 5,000 miles per hour and altitudes in excess of 500,000 feet with the addition of two huge drop tanks. The extra fuel will permit the mammoth engine to burn for a period of 145 seconds, in contrast to a former burning time of 85 seconds.

higher speed ranges.

Although it is reasonably certain that the present versions of the X-15 will never fly in orbit, she has made more significant contributions to space flight than any other manned vehicle, other than those that have been in orbit. X-15 flights furnished the lion's share of our knowledge of weightlessness prior to the first of the Mercury flights. She was foremost in exploring the control of space vehicles with reaction jets, long before the first Mercury astronaut got off the pad. Her pilots pioneered the space suits which future astronauts would require for orbital flights. The stresses placed on the pilots of this aero space craft (a vehicle which can fly in or out of the atmosphere) were of interest to the flight surgeons who would conduct the medical aspects of the future space programs. The contributions of the X-15 to the realm of space flight have overshadowed her valuable contributions to the more mundane world of conventional aviation. The metals of her structure have played a major role in keeping the United States out in front, not only in military aviation, but civilian aviation as well. When the great supersonic transport is placed in service, few people will look back and realize how indispensably this small but stalwart rocket craft

This delta-winged version of the X-15 is being considered as a means to increase its speed and altitude capabilities.

has served in pioneering the way.

Not content to rest on their many laurels, X-15 engineers have even bolder ventures planned for this uncanny flying machine. Two huge tanks have been slung to her sides to hold fuel which will give the rocket engine life for a few additional seconds, precious seconds which many engineers believe may propel her to a hundred miles above the earth and to speeds of more than 6,000 miles per hour.

There are proponents of orbital space flight for the X-15, and these convictions did not occur as afterthoughts to the resounding success that she has enjoyed to date. In the initial phases of conception, many engineers wanted to go for the ultimate with their unusual aircraft and groom her for orbital space flight. Other engineers in the development cycle wanted to construct the bird from the ground up, with delta-shaped wings instead of the more conventional ones which she presently possesses. There is a trend toward this objective at the present, and very serious consideration is being given to the modification of one of the craft to delta configuration. This design the sponsors are confident will permit the X-15 to soar into much higher speed ranges and possibly bolder ventures into suborbital or one-orbit missions around the earth.

It is interesting to note that the Air Force has already awarded astronauts' wings to all Air Force pilots who have flown the X-15 to an altitude of more than 50 miles.

With these new approaches, the X-15 will no doubt go on to even greater achievements in the exploration of space and that very important although neglected, environment which lies between pure space flight and atmospheric flight. She will probably be the last of her kind insofar as resembling what we now refer to as a winged craft is concerned, because the current trend in designs leans, for a very practical reason, toward vehicles which tend to combine the wings and the fuselage into a single shape similar to the delta shape just cited. But one thing is certain, the X-15 has made her mark. Her accomplishments would have been more outstanding and distinct had the more ambitious space projects, such as Mercury, Gemini, and Apollo, not occurred in its time frame. If one had to single out the most important single contribution the black bird made, it was, in all probability, the pioneering of controllable flight back from space into the atmosphere to a landing made absolutely at the discretion of the pilot.

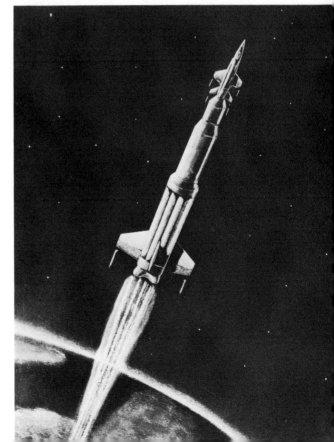

An early engineering concept which would have called for the mating of the X-15 with one of the larger space boosters to permit it to fly in orbit. Several engineering breakthroughs would have been necessary before a flight such as this could have occurred.

10

Waning Wings

The termination of the X-15 program will probably end the era of winged-rocket airplanes as we presently define them. A new type of craft has already arrived on the scene. The designers call these lifting bodies. They, too, will be placed in the category classified as aero spacecraft—that is, they will have the dual capability of operating in and out of the atmosphere.

The unique design of the lifting body makes it difficult to tell where the wings of the craft begin and the fuselage ends, or vice versa. The reason for this radical departure in design is a very practical one. This craft will fill the need for a vehicle that falls between the ballistic characteristics of the Mercury, Gemini, and Apollo space craft and those of the X-15. She will be capable of operating within the atmosphere and will ultimately be capable of orbital flight. But, unlike her forerunners, it can be flown back for a conventional landing, rather than plunging down into the Pacific or Atlantic Ocean under the canopy of a parachute. The shape of this craft is designed to blend selectively most of the desirable attributes for flight in space and in the atmosphere into a single utilitarian space craft.

In short, these recent efforts are intended to make space flight a more simple and less expensive venture for the future. Their arrival will no doubt hasten the exploitation of this new dimension of space on a large scale.

The first serious undertaking to build such a craft took shape in the early fifties in a project which was labeled Dyna Soar. This is not to be confused with the prehistoric monster. It was the name given a vehicle which would have been capable of flight in orbit, and with the versatile ability to return to an air base of the pilot's choice on the entire North American continent. The name Dyna stands for dynamic. The Soar obviously indicates the ability to soar or to glide. Actually, Dyna Soar grew out of the Saenger concept of skipping off the atmosphere in order to circle the entire globe. There were no launching vehicles at its earliest inception capable of placing the Dyna Soar in orbit, therefore the same plan as that conceived for the Saenger bomber—global atmospheric skipping—was also planned for the first earth-circling efforts after two or three suborbital preliminary flights down the Atlantic Missile Range from then Cape Canaveral, Florida, from which to gather basic data prior to an orbital attempt.

These plans were modified later, for in the late 1950s the Air Force was given a green light to develop a booster which, in addition to many other roles, would have had sufficient thrust to place the Dyna Soar in orbit, hence the skipping concept could be abandoned. This booster was designated the Titan III-C. Originally, its center core was intended only as the launching vehicle for the Dyna Soar, but a decision was made to add two massive solid boosters, one on either side of the liquid core. These would give the Titan more than two and a half million pounds of thrust—more than enough power to place this revolutionary craft into a high orbit.

Although great strides were made in developing much of the technology which would permit the Dyna Soar to fly, its fate was sealed in a rather lengthy debate as to the need for such a craft involving the Congress, the Air Force, and the Department of Defense. In 1963 Secretary of Defense Robert S. McNamara made a final decision to cancel the program, and with that decision went the Air Force's first aspirations and efforts at manned space flight.

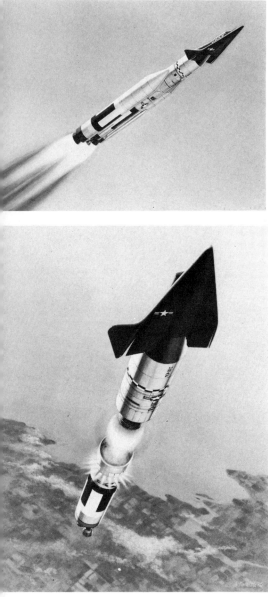

The above sequence shows how the Dyna Soar would have been launched in artist's concept. (*Top left*) The Titan III booster would have hurled the spacecraft toward orbit. (*Top right*) The solid boosters would have been dropped after the fuel was spent. (*Lower left*) Dyna Soar and adapter stage would have separated from the liquid core Titan vehicle which furnished the final push to place it in orbit. (*Lower right*) After final maneuvers to acquire the desired orbit, the Dyna Soar would have been on its own. For the re-entry maneuver the Dyna Soar pilot would have merely turned the spacecraft around and fired the rocket unit in the tail to serve as his retro braking apparatus.

The cancelation of the program was disappointing to many of its staunch advocates who believed that in the long run this was the most practical and the least expensive method of making use of the medium in which man now found that he should be operating. A number of these people predicted that once the flurry of the space race between the United States and the Soviet Union settled down, the ballistic-type space craft, such as Mercury and Gemini and the Vostoks, would run their courses—the circle would turn and the world would see the return of flyable vehicles which the Dyna Soar represented. All advocates of the flyable vehicles concede that for lunar and planetary missions this type vehicle is unnecessary for such missions will not occur with great frequency in the immediate future and present knowledge indicates that the atmospheres of the moon and those planets which are now being considered for the earliest exploration do not lend themselves to winged flight, either for lack of an atmosphere or because of doubts as to the existence of an atmosphere dense enough to support a flyable craft. The argument for winged craft centers primarily around their use for near-earth orbital missions and the practical space roles which will no doubt unfold as our knowledge and technology grows.

There are heartening signs that the circle predicted by the pro-Dyna Soar group has turned and, with the conclusion of the Mercury and Gemini programs, many scientists and engineers are searching for new ways further to refine the techniques of space flight. Obviously, they are looking in the direction of winged craft or lifting bodies because these new configurations are showing up in large numbers on the drawing boards. In fact, some have actually been constructed and are being flown.

The first serious research effort conducted in the United States began in 1957. A team headed by Dr. Alfred J. Eggers of NACA —predecessor to NASA—felt that a flyable shape for re-entry from orbit was not only desirable but would have extensive application in futuristic space flight. For five years the group tested a wide variety of possible space craft shapes in the Ames Research Center's wind tunnels. These tests produced the first extensively detailed data relating lift, drag stability, and heating to re-entry at orbital speeds

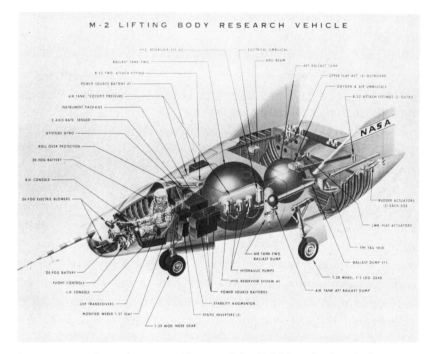

Cutaway view shows the general layout of the M-2 lifting body vehicle.

—speeds on the order of 17,500 miles per hour. One of the models this group tested was a short, broad, 30-degree half cone that was intended to fly apex first. Eggers designated it the M-1 and found it surprisingly successful for re-entry at orbital speeds. However, it was unflyable at the lower speeds such as those at which it would land. This was owing to those forces that contribute to aerodynamic stability or instability and are completely different in effect at low speeds than at high speeds.

Another model tested by Eggers in the wind tunnels was a moderately slender 13-degree half cone which resembled an ice-cream cone cut in half, and it showed some promise. However, the sharper nose caused the temperatures on its surface to soar to intolerable peaks, and the shape also proved to be rather unstable. Eggers then proceeded to round off the nose and carve off the blunt aft end in hopes of enhancing the aerodynamic flow. Not content with the stability characteristics of the model even after these changes, he decided to add two vertical fins, which brought about the desired lateral stability.

With the conceptual groundwork laid, the first lifting body built in the United States was designated the M2-F1. It was flown at Edwards Air Force Base in 1963, towed aloft by an ancient C-47 transport. The half cone-shaped craft was flown by NASA test pilot Milton Thompson, who was one of six pilots originally assigned to the Dyna Soar program. After being towed to altitude behind the lumbering C-47 and released, Thompson piloted the strange craft back to the dry lake at Edwards.

To simplify construction—and of course in the name of time and economy—the first model was built of plywood with a highly polished exterior, to permit a smooth air flow around its futuristic shape. Its only power was a solid-fuel rocket unit—actually a take-off unit used by Air Force bombers and fighters to get off the ground with heavy loads, or to get out of extremely small fields. However, in this case the unit was for use only in case the pilot should be landing short of the field and in need of an auxiliary push in order to make it to within the intended perimeter. As an additional safety feature, the flying motorboat, as people sometimes referred to the M2-F1 with its unorthodox shape, was equipped with an ejection seat for the pilot. This seat, called the "zero ejection seat," would permit him to eject even after the craft had

Dubbed the flying bathtub, the M2-F1 was the first lifting body to fly in the United States. The strange-looking craft was towed to altitude by a C-47 transport aircraft and released for a glide back to Edwards Air Force Base.

Chuck Yeager, the first pilot to break the sound barrier, in the cockpit of the M-2, being briefed on its flight characteristics by Milton Thompson, who is the primary pilot for NASA's lifting-body program.

touched down on the runway—hence at zero altitude.

After proving that the design did have merit in that it responded to control by the pilot as had been predicted, NASA decided to build a more advanced version of the craft. The newer version was constructed of aluminum and featured some changes in the control system, such as the removal of the small elevators which were attached to the outsides of the rudders of its M2-F1 predecessor. Other changes were made in general layout of the cockpit and slight changes in the contour of the over-all configuration. The M2-F2 also featured retractable landing gear in contrast to the fixed gear on the earlier model.

On June 15, 1965, the M2-F2 was rolled out of the Northrop Corporation's plant and turned over to NASA for subsequent flight tests. One of these flights inadvertently confirmed one of the great inherent advantages of the craft's construction other than the mere ability to fly. On May 10, 1965, the M2-F2, piloted by NASA test pilot Bruce Peterson, was returning for a landing at Edwards Air Force Base. When he attempted to lower the gears, Peterson discovered to his consternation, that they would not extend. Upon touchdown, the craft began to veer sharply and then to roll. Although it rolled several times at a relatively high speed, the pilot escaped with minor injuries. All of the systems built into this uncanny new bird were found to be still operative. This confirmed, much to the consolation of the engineers, the structural integrity of the design.

Fourteen subsonic flights had been accomplished in the M2-F2 through April 1967. In each case the craft was dropped from a

B-52 mother aircraft at altitudes of around 45,000 feet. The highest speed attained was .75 mach, which means that even without power the M2-F2 attained a speed of 75 per cent of the speed of sound.

Spurred on by the success of the wooden structural M2-F2, the Northrop Corporation was called to build an aluminum version in this growing series. This model was designated the HL-10, with the HL standing for horizontal landing. The HL-10 differs considerably in configuration from the M2-F2, with the major differences in the over-all contour, the cockpit design, and the controls. For increased stability the NASA engineers decided to add a third vertical stabilizer. This rudder was also designed to serve the dual purpose of controlling the craft laterally and can be spread out to serve as a braking flap on landing. To accomplish this, the rudder was made as a split unit, the two halves of which pivot in unison when it serves as a rudder. When the need arises for it to be used as a braking device, the unit is spread apart by electrical actuators and presents a rather sizable frontal area for air braking.

The M2-F2 and the HL-10 both have been fitted with hydrogen-peroxide rocket units adapted from the Lunar Landing Research Vehicle—a craft in which the astronauts rehearse lunar landings. This device will be used to extend the landing approach if necessary.

In order to drive the HL-10 farther up the speed spectrum a

The perspective drawings, right, show basic differences between the M2-F2 (left) and the HL-10 (right).

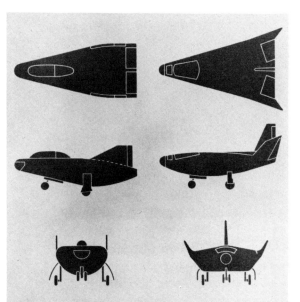

Basic configuration of M2-F2 *and* HL-10

power plant had to be selected and fitted to its rather unique air frame. Since all of these unusual craft were being built on a very low-priority, and an extremely small budget, it was considered rather unrealistic that NASA could award another contract for the development of a new power unit tailored specifically for use in this bird. Recalling the success of the power plant of the X-1, they decided to press one of these units back into service to power the HL-10. This was certainly indicative of the quality of the performance of an engine which was twenty years old being brought back for use in such a sophisticated new venture. Through the use of this system the HL-10 can be launched from under the wing of the B-52 and attain speeds on the order of mach 1.5 and 2.0 and reach for altitudes beyond 80,000 feet—which very closely approximates a spacelike environment. This ability to go faster and higher will give the engineers an opportunity to evaluate the pilot's con-

One of the most sophisticated of the lifting bodies is the HL-10, built by Northrop Corporation. It has a lift to drag ratio of 4, which means that for every four feet of horizontal travel the craft sinks or descends one foot.

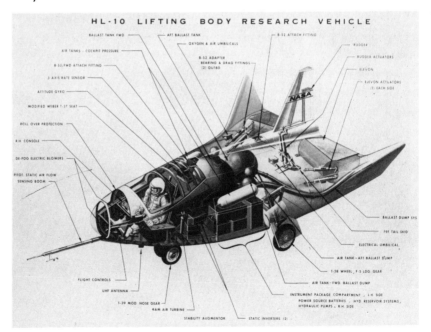

HL-10 LIFTING BODY RESEARCH VEHICLE

The HL-10 tucked under the wing of the B-52 mother plane, heads into the California skies for another test flight to gather data which will find use in the design of futuristic vehicles.

trol of this bizarre vehicle and will give them some insight on how these configurations will best compete with ballistic shapes for space roles of the future.

Experts at Northrop Corporation, in a study contract conducted in behalf of the National Aeronautics and Space Administration, have come up with a rather bold plan which has been dubbed Minimum Manned Lifting Body Entry Vehicle Study. The plan proposes that an advanced version of the M-2 or the HL-10 be launched by a Titan II rocket—the same booster which orbited all of the Gemini astronauts. The flight would encompass only about 90 per cent of the globe for it would be brought back to earth from this partial orbit to a piloted landing at Edwards Air Force Base which has seen so many exotic aircraft return from similarly bold ventures.

Prior to the execution of such a flight several innovations would have to be incorporated into the new craft. An advanced heat shield to withstand the searing heat of re-entry would have to be developed, and Northrop proposes the use of a honeycombed material to which they have devoted considerable time and expense in perfecting. This material can be bonded directly to the aluminum skin of the vehicles, with essentially the same configurations as the M2-F2 or the HL-10. Other significant features which would have to be built into the craft would include a heat-resistant canopy and windshield somewhat like that of the X-15 with jettisonable heat shielding over the glass panels: a Gemini ejection seat affording the

Northrop Corporation has proposed the launching of an advanced manned version of the HL-10 into a partial orbit of the earth with a planned landing of the craft at Edwards Air Force Base, California. The launch vehicle would be the Titan II, which launched the series of Gemini flights.

pilot the ability to eject from the craft on the launching pad should the booster be in imminent danger of explosion on the pad or just after lift off. In Northrop's conceptual version the engineers have recommended a two-axis side stick controller and skid-type main landing gear, the latter of which has been utilized so effectively on the X-15 and the X-2 in years gone by.

In an effort to shrink the time for the lifting body to be introduced into the space arena, another plan proposes that an unmanned version of the M2-F2 or the HL-10 be flown under the auspices of the Apollo Applications Program, wherein a number of areas of interest are to be explored. This will be a follow-on to the moon program. Over a period of time several lifting bodies would be flown aboard the Saturn booster, in a compartment which would have been occupied formerly by the Lunar Excursion Module, on earlier pre-lunar landing shakedown flights. At a point in orbit, the shrouds would be blown off and the lifting body freed to begin its predetermined return trip earthward, under remote radio control for a landing at Edwards Air Force Base, California.

Not to be deterred by the loss of the Dyna Soar program, the Air Force has initiated other projects to explore the lifting body design, anticipating the day when a vehicle such as this might have a very practical defense application, should space ever become an arena for military operations. The program began with a series of pilotless space craft flown down the Atlantic missile ranges to explore their characteristics of maneuverability and the ability to withstand the searing heat generated on their skin as they plunge down the re-entry corridors. Heat is the major adversary to flight with this kind of vehicle. Flyable space craft descend at a slower rate than ballistic craft because of the increased atmospheric drag which is exerted on them. This prolongs the period to which they are subjected to these temperatures extremes. The most difficult technical problems to surmount have been in the area of the development of materials which could withstand such heat. For instance, the nose cap which would have flown on the Dyna Soar glider would have had to withstand temperatures as high as 5,000 degrees

Project ASSET, which has been one of the most successful unmanned lifting-body efforts to date, explored re-entry problem areas as a prelude to manned flights into space aboard lifting bodies. The ASSET vehicle is shown mounted atop its Thor booster in this launch from Cape Kennedy.

Glowing white-hot from 3000-degree heat, an SV-5 maneuverable lifting body heads earthward as it returns from space in this artist's concept. Maneuver outside the earth's atmosphere is accomplished by small gas jets. Within the atmosphere, two flap devices mounted at the rear exert aerodynamic control.

F. But as the space programs have progressed, valuable knowledge and technical breakthroughs in the metallurgical field have been brought about to the degree that aero and astronautical engineers are more optimistic than ever that winged or flyable re-entries can be made safely and routinely.

The Air Force program to investigate this area of flight has been designated START, which stands for Spacecraft Technology and Advanced Re-entry Tests. Data acquired from these projects may find future use in both manned and unmanned space flights. The earliest of these ventures involved the firing down the Atlantic Test Range of an unmanned vehicle called ASSET, built by the Mc-Donnell Aircraft Corporation. The word ASSET was derived from the initial letters of a very lengthy engineering term—Aerothermo-dynamicelastic Structural Systems Environmental Tests. Simply stated, it means experimentation with and exploration of problems associated with a re-entering flyable vehicle.

The second phase of the program is called PRIME. This stands for Precision, Recovery, Including Maneuvering Entry. The latter program also uses an unmanned vehicle, the SV-5, built by the Martin Company, which has been flown on an Atlas booster down the Pacific Test Range and maneuvered as it re-entered from space, traveling hundreds of miles off the original course it was following when it re-entered. The SV-5D vehicle was retrieved in the vicinity of the island of Kwajelein, some 4,400 miles down range from Vandenberg Air Force Base, California, the point from which it was launched.

Air Force planners obviously feeling confident as the result of such satisfactory unmanned endeavors, awarded a contract to Martin to build a manned version of the SV-5D design called the X-24-A, to be flown from under the wing of the same B-52 bomber which has lugged the X-15, the M2-F2, and the HL-10 aloft on so many prior occasions. From high over California it will be dropped, at which time the pilot will fire up the XLR-11 rocket engine, another of the X-1 engines which has won so many earlier laurels. The power of this engine should propel the craft to an altitude of around 100,000 feet and to a speed of around 1400 miles per hour.

These photographs show the Air Force's X-24-A entry into the lifting body program. The four nozzles seen just below the mid rudder of this futuristic craft are the business end of the XLR-11 rocket motor, the same motor which propelled the famous X-1 through the sound barrier on October 14, 1947. This very reliable rocket workhorse is built by Reaction Motors.

The Martin X-24-A lifting body, which is also referred to as PILOT (for Piloted Low Speed Test), is another in the series of vehicles designed to pioneer a new method of space flight.

After the energy of its propellants has been spent, its pilot will turn it toward Edwards Air Force Base and perform a series of pre-programmed maneuvers as he returns in order to get a feel for its control characteristics and to evaluate other aspects of the flight. He will then land it dead stick on the dry lake bed as the other lifting bodies land.

The trend in futuristic space vehicles is rather firmly established at present. It points to lifting bodies designed along the lines of the pioneering Dyna Soar, the M2-F2, the HL-10, the X-24, and the

The illustration (opposite right) shows one of the many futuristic missions planned for vehicles like the X-24, missions such as re-supply of space stations, satellite repair, rescue of stranded or ill astronauts and the interception and inspection of potentially hostile satellites or manned spacecraft.

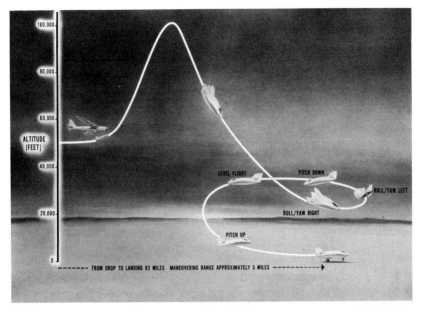

Illustration above shows the flight profile of the Air Force entry into the lifting body field of flight. A rocket engine drives the X-24-A to the pinnacle of her flight after which the pilot will maneuver her back to Edwards Air Force Base from which the flight originated.

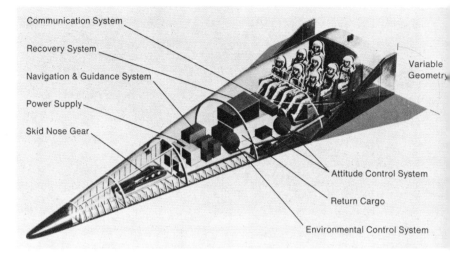

Communication System

Recovery System

Navigation & Guidance System

Power Supply

Skid Nose Gear

Variable Geometry

Attitude Control System

Return Cargo

Environmental Control System

A concept proposed by Northrop Corporation would be capable of shuttling crews to and from space stations or possibly retrieving astronauts who might be stranded in orbit. Visionaries see many roles for such a craft.

other aero space craft which bear such close resemblance. Most of the astronauts subscribe to this approach to routine space flight, for they are, in the main, test pilots who have known and spent much of their time in the air in complete control of the vehicles which they were flying. Mercury, Gemini, and Apollo, as great as their contributions have been to space-flight experience and no doubt will be in the future, were ballistic in nature, with the inevitable return under the canopy of a parachute. Captain Walter Schirra, who flew in both the Mercury and Gemini programs, had this to say at an annual meeting of the Society of Experimental Test Pilots when asked what he thought about lifting bodies and their role in the future: "There is nothing more ignominious than for a test pilot to return to earth under the canopy of a parachute."

It is believed that without doubt these sentiments are shared almost to the man by the other members of the astronaut corps. What better endorsement could there be as to the more appropriate space route to take, especially in the practical exploitation of that near ocean of space encircling the earth into which man will ultimately thrust himself with great frequency on a myriad of missions?

11

"Flying to and from Space"

If the new arena of near earth space is ever to be used in a practical manner, we must develop more practical vehicles with which to traverse it. This means that we must have vehicles capable of carrying larger payloads and more people, in addition to being able to land them routinely in a conventional and safe manner, not under the shroud of a parachute. In short, most experts agree that we need a space craft that will operate with characteristics similar to those of the modern-day aircraft.

There have been many concepts offered for the creation of such a craft, but the most popular version is known as the aerospace plane. The title of this vehicle identifies its operating characteristics. The "aero" indicates that it would possess the ability to fly in the atmosphere and the "space," of course, denotes that it would also be capable of orbital or suborbital flight.

Although most of the concepts differ in varying degrees, they all have one thing in common: they offer to meet the requirement that the craft will have the ability to fly back through the atmosphere to a conventional landing.

One of the earliest proposals for such a unique craft was made by Dr. Walter Dornberger, formerly General Dornberger, who directed Germany's development of the V-2 rocket. Dr. Dornberger came to the United States after World War II and served as an adviser to the government on the ballistic-missile program. He was also a major and probably the most influential force in attempting to interest this nation in building a Dyna Soar type space craft, or a rocket-powered winged vehicle. He was, unquestionably, one of the world's most visionary space advocates, and he spoke from the vantage point of great personal experience.

Dr. Dornberger and other engineers and scientists of the Bell Aerosystems Corporation visualized a vehicle which would bear a distinct resemblance to the Dyna Soar. It would be mounted atop a flying booster—in reality a huge aircraft. The booster, however, would possess propulsion units which would greatly expand the operating characteristics of existing engines. Although these would be jet-power in nature, they would differ in that they would probably operate in three different propulsive cycles instead of one or two. They would take off using a jet cycle almost identical to present-day engines, but with considerably greater efficiency, based simply on normal improvements in engine manufacture which are bound to occur.

After climbing out to around 50,000 feet altitude they would be put into a second power cycle which would bring to bear a combination of the conventional jet-engine operation gradually transitioning to that of the ram-jet.

The ram-jet is the simplest of all jet-propulsion units in that it derives its compression for combustion from the speed of movement of the vehicle through the air with no requirement for complex turbines or fans. The incoming air simply combines with the fuel, which burns continuously. As the speed of a craft using the ram-jet principle increases, so does the efficiency of the power plant.

When the proposed vehicle of the Bell group approached higher altitudes, the need for the conventional jet unit would diminish and the craft would then be switched over to complete ram-jet power. The ram-jet engines would be capable of propelling the space plane to an altitude of approximately 120,000 feet and to speeds around 5,200 miles per hour. At this point the crew of the hypothetical

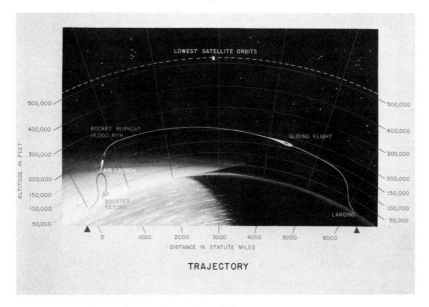

LOWEST SATELLITE ORBITS

ROCKET BURNOUT
14,000 MPH

GLIDING FLIGHT

AIR LAUNCH

BOOSTER
RETURN

LANDING

ALTITUDE IN FEET

500,000
400,000
300,000
200,000
150,000
100,000
50,000

0   1000   2000   3000   4000   5000   6000

DISTANCE IN STATUTE MILES

TRAJECTORY

The diagram shows the flight profile of the Bell Aircraft Corporation's plan conceived by Dr. Walter Dornberger. The aerospacecraft (Artist's Concept below) could reach any continent on earth in an hour or less. Note the booster, in reality a huge aircraft with a more advanced propulsion system. The artist's concept shows how the continent-spanning craft would be launched from a mother aircraft. The latter would return to the home base of operations shortly after the launch of the piggy-back spacecraft.

intercontinental transport would fire the rocket units mounted in the tail of the space craft. The vehicle would move off rapidly along two guide rails from the top of the booster craft and hurl itself on up to an altitude of approximately 40 miles. The speed at this point would be around 15,000 miles per hour, a velocity just under the speed of long-range ballistic missiles. This is more than sufficient to hurl the craft over intercontinental distances. According to Dr. Dornberger's calculations, any spot on earth could be reached in one hour or less.

Over a point located at a considerable distance from the intended destination the pilot would begin the re-entry. This is the most precarious of the maneuvers in intercontinental space flight, for the craft must be very carefully controlled. This is for two very critical reasons. First, the plane would be returning without power, which means that it would be most absolutely essential that the pilot's navigation be flawless in order to arrive at a desired destination. During re-entry, the craft would glide to the desired point. A plan has been considered whereby the space transport would be equipped with one or two small jet engines, in order to give the pilot some

Re-entry of the Bell concept of the rocket transport. Note the glow along the leading edges of the wings generated by the heat of re-entry. These searing temperatures have posed the most formidable problem for the engineers developing such craft.

leeway for maneuvering on the other end of the line and also to make final adjustments for landing. The second and most salient reason for extremely precise control over the craft is that the angle of descent must be exactly right. It cannot be too steep, or the temperatures generated on the leading edges of the wings or the nose would soar beyond the structural limits of the presently available materials. Also, if the re-entry is made too shallow, the heat is too prolonged and the same problem is encountered. Because of the critical nature of the descending phase of the flight, many of the control devices for making such a descent would be completely automatic, with the pilot taking over in the final moments just prior to touchdown. He, of course, could override the automatic system at any time if it should malfunction.

It is easy to see how a transport such as this could change the world. It has been said that such a completely new system of transportation which would bring the people of the world closer together might possibly do more to ease tensions among the nations than any other event which could occur based on the assumption that the close ties allay to some degree innate suspicions and prejudices.

Many of the aerospace companies have investigated designs of space vehicles similar to the one conceived by Dr. Dornberger. However, most of them differ from the original in approach. Lockheed Aircraft has come up with a very detailed concept offering several alternatives in the boost system which will be utilized in order to get an aerospace craft into orbit or into an extremely long-range ballistic flight.

The most novel feature of the Lockheed launch concept will be the large first-stage aircraft, which, although capable of self-sustaining flight—with very powerful jet engines—after launching its charge, will not be able to take off with its on-board power. These power units could not develop sufficient thrust to send the space craft into orbit or even into long-range ballistic flight. Instead, the Lockheed plan calls for the first-stage aircraft to be driven down a rail by conventional rocket power until it reaches a speed of around 450 miles per hour. The on-board rocket engines of the first-stage

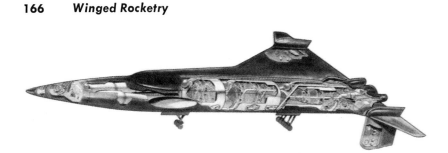

Shown above is a Lockheed Corporation concept for a recoverable booster for flyable spacecraft. The payload-carrying second stage is shown mated to the mother craft in the illustration below. Alignment for launching from the top of the mother craft is achieved by two rails along which the carried craft moves as it fires its on-board rocket engine.

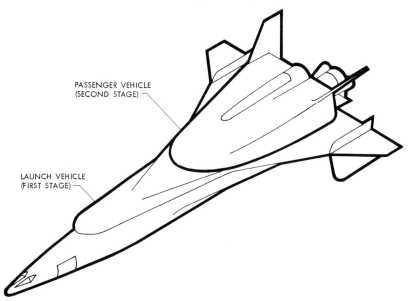

PASSENGER VEHICLE
(SECOND STAGE)

LAUNCH VEHICLE
(FIRST STAGE)

unit will then be fired. They will continue to accelerate the first stage (the mother craft) and second stage (the passenger cargo and crew compartment) until speeds around 4,000 miles per hour are achieved. At about the time when the combined vehicles attain this velocity, they will have arrived at an altitude of around 150,000 feet. They will then separate at this point. The rocket engines of the second stage will then be fired and that stage will continue to accelerate at a phenomenal rate. Meantime, the launching stage will begin a gradual glide back to its base of operation. This can now be done very easily since it has discharged its payload. At an altitude of around 20,000 feet the pilot on board will start conventional jet engines, which will be used in order to fly back for a landing as an ordinary aircraft does.

The upper stage will continue its flight, either as an orbital mission or as a long ballistic arc. Although the latter requires less propulsive power, the speeds generated are still sufficient to hurl the space craft to any continent of the globe in an hour or less.

According to the Lockheed concept, the shape of the upper stage craft can be tailored to fit any mission desired. The aeronautical term for the variations in such a space craft would be L/D, which denotes lift over drag, i.e., the altitude to which a given shape will descend versus the horizontal distance over which it will traverse during a given time interval. If, for instance, a certain craft is referred to as having an L/D of 1, it simply means that the craft will

This diagram shows the general layout of the payload-carrying stage of the Lockheed concept for a flyable aerospacecraft. Note the space apportioned for fuel. This is indicative of the immense quantities required for maneuver in space.

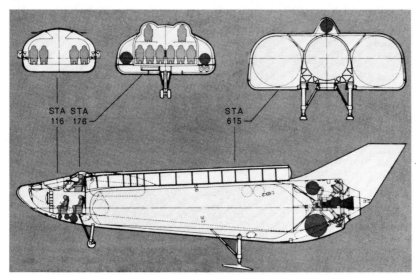

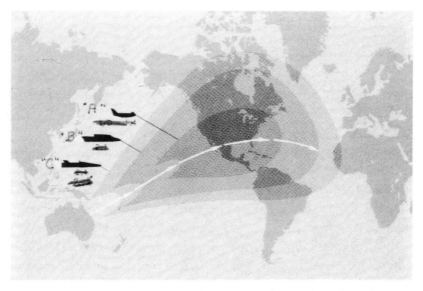

Diagram above depicts possible landing sites on the North and South American continents for spacecraft of varying lift/drag characteristics. The illustration below shows more detailed views of the various shapes and their lift versus drag flying abilities.

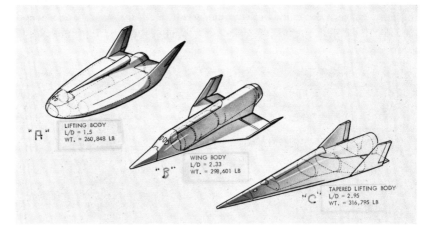

"A" LIFTING BODY
L/D = 1.5
WT. = 260,848 LB

"B" WING BODY
L/D = 2.33
WT. = 298,601 LB

"C" TAPERED LIFTING BODY
L/D = 2.95
WT. = 316,795 LB

cover one horizontal mile for every mile it descends as it returns to earth from orbit. This, of course, only applies after the craft has penetrated the atmosphere and the L/D factor varies with altitude and the constant changes which occur as it descends through varying densities.

Typical examples of the very important role shape plays in the ability of the winged space craft of the United States to maneuver are shown in the accompanying illustration. The higher the L/D number, the wider the lateral and horizontal maneuverability. The slightest maneuver can permit vast distances to be traversed, as may be seen in the illustration, which covers the North American continent. This is referred to as the landing footprint.

Another unique aspect of the Lockheed concept for winged ballistic or orbital flight is to be found in the proposed vertical launching of the space vehicle. This plan also envisions the commercial transportation of passengers. However, there are problems involved which might be disconcerting to the would-be travelers. They would be quite uncomfortable during the initial launching phase, because of the G-forces exerted on them as the rocket engine hurled them vertically aloft. On the other hand, the advantages of such a vertical system are readily apparent. It would be much more economical, because there would be no need for the sled facility which the horizontally launched system requires. This would represent an enormous saving in construction costs as well as in the acquiring of the large land tracts needed for a horizontal operation. The vertical launch technique would be extremely desirable, moreover, if the system were to find acceptance in various military roles.

In other ways, however, the horizontal launching complex would have distinct advantages over the vertical launching plan. The passengers would enjoy a much more comfortable takeoff, for the acceleration of their vehicle would be more gradual than with the vertical plan. There also would be a greater safety factor in the horizontal launching, for the mission could be aborted by various braking arrangements on the sled track, through the use of devices such as water scoops and frictional braking contact with the track itself. In the vertical launching, once the vehicle departed, there would be no turning back and no way to stop the upward movement without great jeopardy to the craft and to the crew and passengers. There would be a very critical interval of time just after launch until the craft could gain sufficient altitude for the pilot to jettison the large quantity of fuel aboard in order that a glide landing back to the home base could be safely executed. If the crew could not get rid of the fuel in an extremely short period of time, the craft would be so heavy that, in all probability, it could not continue to fly and would be doomed to an inevitable plunge back to earth.

There are other concepts for aerospace planes which would effect a compromise between the vertical and horizontal launching methods.

One such plan would be to employ gravity to assist in getting the craft into orbit or into a prolonged ballistic flight. A steep launching ramp would be built, which would send the vehicle, cradled in a rocket-propelled sled, down a veritable mountainside, with or without active propulsive assistance from the on-board power plants. At the bottom of what might be described as a bowl-shaped launching complex, the main power units would be ignited, hurling the craft at a rather pronounced angle up the other side of the "mountain." After the vehicle had attained the maximum speed while still nestled in the sled, the pilot would activate the controls and lift the craft from the cradle. The aerospace plane would now be on its own, with its internal power unit furnishing the thrust for hurling it out of the atmosphere. This plan could be compared to a ski jump, with the exception that the climb up the other side of the bowl would be made at a steeper angle. The major technical difficulties to overcome in this type of launching system would be concerned with a method of reducing the intense friction which the weight of the sled and the space vehicle would generate on those points where the sled and the rail would make contact. Dr. Saenger had already anticipated this problem when he conceived the antipodal bomber. It was for this reason that he assigned a number of experts in lubricants to try to devise a means of overcoming or minimizing the dangerous friction problem.

It might be added that Saenger had also considered the slide down the "mountainside" and coast up the other slope technique as a possible way to launch the antipodal bomber. This might account for recurring reports that the Russians have considered a craft which would utilize this method of becoming space-borne. There is little

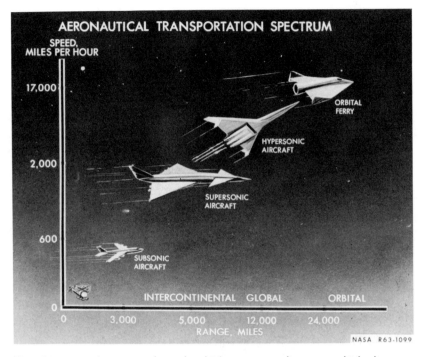

AERONAUTICAL TRANSPORTATION SPECTRUM

SPEED,
MILES PER HOUR

17,000

2,000

600

0

ORBITAL
FERRY

HYPERSONIC
AIRCRAFT

SUPERSONIC
AIRCRAFT

SUBSONIC
AIRCRAFT

INTERCONTINENTAL   GLOBAL   ORBITAL

0   3,000   5,000   12,000   24,000
RANGE, MILES

NASA R63-1099

This diagram relates speeds and vehicle types to distances which they can span.

doubt that the German scientists who were captured by the Soviets after World War II had a significant impact on future Soviet thought and contributed much know-how and technical assistance in space flight, research, and development.

One important facet of the launching down the "mountainside" concept is the fact that, should difficulties be encountered as the craft moves down the ramp, the pilot could forego the normal application of power at the bottom and dissipate the energy which the vehicle had acquired at this point by letting it coast to a stop while mounting the other side. Braking could be more fully assured by fitting small retrorockets to the sled, facing forward. These would effectively assist in the slowing or stopping action. The latter technique is considered essential for the horizontal launching method in any arrangement.

Thus far, all the plans for getting our flyable space craft into orbit have been presented with great technical hurdles to surmount and this no doubt will remain the case in the immediate future. Ideally, the most desirable craft would be one which could take off from a conventional jet runway and fly into orbit without the use of complex boosters and boost facilities, like those just described. Hopefully, such a craft is unfolding in the minds of many space visionaries.

This is envisioned by most engineers and scientists to be, upon completion, about the size of the B-52 bomber or the 707 airliner. It would have to be constructed of very futuristic materials in order to withstand the intensely hot temperatures encountered in return from orbit or near orbit. Experts of the leading metal companies are working diligently to produce such materials.

The power plant of so unique a craft would have to be truly revolutionary to work successfully. Most engineers agree that to fly from a runway into orbit will require three stages of power. As the majority of them see it, the vehicle will take off under conventional jet-engine power and begin a gradual climb to altitude. After attaining an altitude of around 50,000 or 60,000 feet, the pilot will increase the speed considerably, and transition into the second phase of power, the ram-jet phase. The craft can now accelerate to greater speeds with greater efficiency, for the density of the atmosphere has diminished, thus minimizing atmospheric drag. The ram jet is the simplest of all power units because, unlike the regular jet engine in which the air must be compressed by several stages of rotating compressor wheels prior to being ignited, the ram jet engine obtains its compression solely by its movement through the air. This movement however, must be at a very high velocity. In addition to the fantastic speeds of which the ram jet is capable, it can also propel a vehicle to far higher altitudes—altitudes at which the conventional jet engine would be incapable of operating.

After going into the ram-jet mode of operation, the pilot of the aerospace plane would also go into a new sequence of operation. This would have a bearing on the next source of power to which he would have to resort prior to being able to fly into orbit.

This particular plan would utilize an apparatus carried on board

HYPERSONIC CRUISE PROPULSION REQUIREMENTS

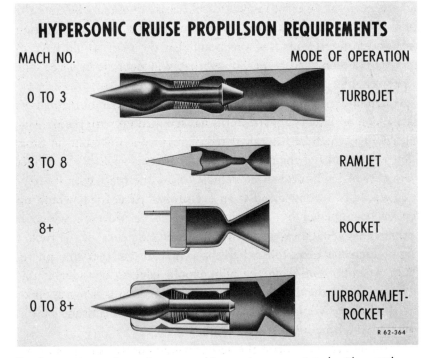

MACH NO.	MODE OF OPERATION
0 TO 3	TURBOJET
3 TO 8	RAMJET
8+	ROCKET
0 TO 8+	TURBORAMJET-ROCKET

R 62-364

The lineup shows the various propulsion systems associated with speeds related to the speed of sound. To fly a vehicle to and from orbit would require the blending of all of these, as shown at the bottom and referred to as the turboramjet-rocket. The use of any one of the systems would depend on particular points in a given flight. For example, the turbojet can propel an aircraft very effectively to altitudes in the vicinity of 60,000 to 70,000 feet. At that point, a ramjet type propulsion system would be essential to increase a craft's velocity. Upon reaching the fringes of the atmosphere and beyond, only a rocket type power plant can be utilized as a source of propulsion.

which would be capable of liquefying the oxygen through which the aircraft moves and storing it on board. It can readily be seen how practical this would be. The weight of the vehicle would be diminishing, owing to the rapid rate at which it would be burning fuel to acquire higher speeds. The replacement of this weight with liquid oxygen would permit the pilot to acquire a new form of fuel for his third mode of power, which he would employ later. As he climbs farther and farther toward the outer fringes of the atmosphere, even the efficient ram-jet would cease to operate because the air would become so rarefied that it could not support combustion or aerodynamic lift. It is at this point that the pilot would have to resort to the only form of power that will operate in space—the rocket engine.

When he arrives in the vacuum of space he can combine the oxygen which his liquefying apparatus has scooped up with the remaining jet fuel which he has calculated to retain for this point in time. He then would fire the combination of the two fuels in the rocket chambers of his hybrid space vehicle. Now the craft with its payload would be hurled ahead at an even faster pace, for it would no longer be impeded by the friction of the air through which it formerly moved. Since, as stated earlier, the efficiency of the rocket engine increases manyfold when the vehicle leaves the atmosphere, the most important thing the pilot would have to consider at this point would be the direction in which the thrust was being applied, for this action would determine the plane and the altitude of the orbit in which he intends to operate.

Upon his arrival in orbit the aerodynamic control surfaces of his craft would be rendered useless and have no bearing on control. The pilot must now utilize small reaction jets to maneuver. However, these miniature rocket units require considerable fuel, so he would have to use them sparingly in order to conserve a sizable quantity of the fuel for use in the retrofire, which would brake the velocity of his craft sufficiently to make it fall back toward the earth. He must also save enough fuel to align the vehicle for re-entry, which is always a most critical phase of the flight.

One of the most pressing needs in orbital flight today is the ability to shift his craft from one orbital plane to another, i.e., the track of the orbit in which the pilot desires to fly. This is much more difficult than it would appear on the surface. A pilot cannot just turn his space craft, apply power, and move over into a new orbital plane. That is to say, he cannot perform such a maneuver today to any effective degree because the power requirements are still beyond man's present technology. For example, to make a 15-degree change in the orbital plane of a space craft using present-day propellents would require that the latter be equivalent to 60 per cent of the weight of the vehicle. The weight of existing space craft and their payloads has always been and continues to be a matter of serious concern, so it is rather obvious that conventional space flight will not permit maneuvers such as large plane changes for many years to come—that is, not until new power sources or new techniques are developed. This is one very important reason why the effective gathering of fuel en route to orbit could possibly become the answer to the very complex problem of maneuver in space.

A more advanced plan for the aerospace plane is one in which the craft's apparatus not only liquefies oxygen, but takes on hydrogen in the same fashion. These ingredients, when fired in combination, make for a much more potent fuel combination than the kerosene-oxygen mixture. The fact that the use of these ingredients does not start until the craft has reached the fringes of the atmosphere also means that they will have to burn for only a short duration to push the vehicle to orbital speeds, thus saving the remaining fuel for possible maneuver in orbit. The greatest advantage in the use of this last technique is the fact that for all practical purposes the spacecraft has acquired fuel en route for use out of the atmosphere which it did not originally take along.

The vast technical strides taken already and the increasing frequency of manned space flights point to the day when such flights will become rather commonplace. This will inevitably bring about a need to be able to fly out there with ease and safety, in order to perform practical missions—missions similar to those which aircraft now perform within the atmosphere, such as rescue and defense. It is very conceivable that one day a catastrophe in space will drive home the need for a craft that can fly into orbit, maneuver into a rendezvous with a stranded craft, and take its astronaut crew on board for a safe return to earth. Many space planners also envision the day when there might be occasion to look over the intent of foreign space craft or satellites moving aloft whose roles might be hostile in nature. A space plane equipped with sensitive inspection equipment, such as radar, remote television, and radiation detection devices could rendezvous with suspect craft and evaluate their roles or intentions, just as NORAD does with ground based apparatus to a more limited degree today.

Realizing the shortcomings of the power plants and the inability to change the orbital planes entirely at the discretion of the crew owing to these limitations, the aerospace engineers have come up with a partial compromise solution which calls on the most basic of aeronautical controls as a means of permitting the crew to shift their craft into a new orbital plane.

Let us take a hypothetical look at some possible missions which say a military aerospace plane crew would be called upon to perform sometime in the not too distant future. Suppose crew X, on alert as a part of the Space Defense Force of the United States, has been scrambled into orbit to look over a newly orbited satellite whose weight and size are determined to be quite irregular when evaluated in contrast to previously launched satellites hence more suspect. As they climb out to the suspect satellites orbital altitude, transitioning into the various power modes and taking on board liquid oxygen and hydrogen, they take up a heading which should place them within the vicinity of the suspect craft—in order to look it over. After a half-hour or so of flight—and the many complex procedures associated therewith, they arrive in orbit and reasonably near the strange craft. However, a radar fix confirms that they are forty miles to the left of their objective. They are immediately aware of the fact that to make a change of plane to that degree is beyond the power of the propellents which they have stored on the way up. In the light of the new procedures they have had to learn as a part of these new Space Defense Force operations, they know that the only alternative for them if they are to effect the interception is to fire their retro rockets and descend again into the atmosphere and start anew. Now, however, with a newly introduced operating concept, they do not have to descend all the way to their point of origin. They merely have to dip down into a reasonably dense region of the atmosphere, go through another oxygen and hydrogen liquefying cycle, then climb back out on a new heading which will place them in alignment with the craft which they were unable to intercept on the last try. The important point is that

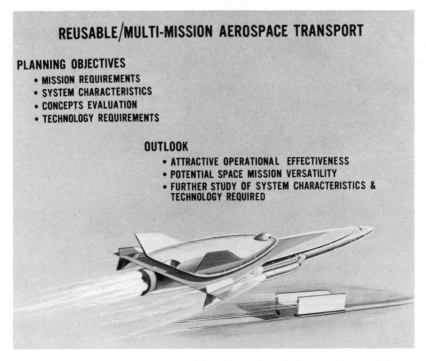

REUSABLE/MULTI-MISSION AEROSPACE TRANSPORT

PLANNING OBJECTIVES
- MISSION REQUIREMENTS
- SYSTEM CHARACTERISTICS
- CONCEPTS EVALUATION
- TECHNOLOGY REQUIREMENTS

OUTLOOK
- ATTRACTIVE OPERATIONAL EFFECTIVENESS
- POTENTIAL SPACE MISSION VERSATILITY
- FURTHER STUDY OF SYSTEM CHARACTERISTICS & TECHNOLOGY REQUIRED

Aerospace Transport as envisioned by the National Aeronautics and Space Administration. Note the cradle from which the craft has just lifted after take-off.

they made the correction to arrive on the new heading aerodynamically—that is, by means of conventional airplane controls. Of course, the lost time might sometimes be extremely critical, but until the day comes when power breakthroughs such as more sophisticated nuclear propulsion or some yet to be discovered power sources are available, it appears as though man must resort to already proven methods in order to move at his discretion in space no matter how basic in nature those methods may be.

Another concept which has gained a considerable following in the aerospace industry is the tanker-type operation for aerospace planes. If the aerospace dilemma which we just described had occurred to a space craft of this design, one which did not embody the liquefying apparatus on board operating on kerosene and oxygen in order to arrive in orbit, a different approach to orbital plane change

Artist's concept of a reusable passenger ferry vehicle with the payload, an integral part of the second stage, mounted "piggyback" on the booster. Both stages of the horizontal take-off (HTO) vehicle would be flown back to earth base for re-use.

would have to be adapted. After aborting the interception the more conventional craft would descend again into the atmosphere and rendezvous with a tanker craft. The two would hook up, just as the military bombers and fighters do so frequently today. The aerospace plane would take on board a vast quantity of kerosene and oxygen—disconnect, make the necessary orbital heading correction aerodynamically, and climb back out to make the desired interception.

Another very constructive role for the aerospace plane might be the shuttling of technicians and workers to build space stations or to repair satellites, such as those employed in the very important role of world-wide communications. This would eliminate the extremely expensive process of launching still another satellite, with the attendant need for another oneway booster to place it in orbit, plus the cost of the new satellite itself. Instead all that might have been required were fresh solar cells to renew the power source of the original satellite or perhaps the mere replacement of a very inexpensive part to make it operative once again.

To perform tasks such as those just cited, with ballistic craft, means the spending of additional rockets which cannot be returned for use again and the deployment of a large recovery force to retrieve the astronauts upon their return. It also means that to ready another flight, even in the midst of a pressing emergency, would require weeks of preparation with the current space craft and boosters, whereas only hours or even minutes would be needed if there existed a practical aerospace plane for such missions.

As so many of America's astronauts will agree, "there is nothing more ignominious"—and many add "more expensive"—than for skilled test pilots, who are so ably represented within the astronauts corps, "to return to earth from orbit under the shroud of a parachute," when they could be winging their way to and from orbit, just as they wing their way so adeptly from the Manned Space Craft Center in Houston, Texas, to Cape Kennedy, Florida, in conventional fighter planes.

There is little doubt that when this very advanced technology is brought about through diligent research—and more space flight experience has been acquired—the day will come when there will be winged armadas shuttling to and from orbit. All factors point to wings—or flyable rocket vehicles, if you will—serving as the all-important link between earth and orbit. I am sure that when that day comes all astronauts will welcome the opportunity to fly to and from the new and endless dimensions of space, instead of being hurled there on the nose of a one-way rocket and then falling back to earth with little or no control of the space craft.

Much diligent thought and many laborious hours of research and engineering are being devoted to acquiring the ability to fly in a practical way within the atmosphere and into space. The drawing below is an indication of things to come.

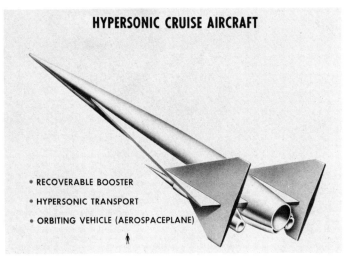

HYPERSONIC CRUISE AIRCRAFT

- RECOVERABLE BOOSTER
- HYPERSONIC TRANSPORT
- ORBITING VEHICLE (AEROSPACEPLANE)

Index

181

MAJOR JAMES C. SPARKS, USAF (RET.)

was born in Birmingham, Alabama, and educated in the Public Schools there. As a youngster he was an avid builder of model airplanes and had great curiosity about science and astronomy.

He entered Air Force flight training in 1943 and flew thirty-five missions over Germany with the Eighth Air Force. Upon discharge, he resumed his education until he was recalled to active duty, to fly in the Berlin Airlift. He later joined the American Forces Network in Germany, as an announcer-newscaster. After returning to the United States, he entered commercial radio as a newscaster.

In the Fall of 1951, he was again recalled to active service, during the Korean War, and flew tours of duty with the Strategic Air Command and the Aerospace Rescue and Recovery Service.

In 1957, he was assigned to the Office of Information of the Office of the Secretary of Air Force, in New York City and at the Pentagon, in Washington, D.C., positions he held until his retirement in 1967. During this tour he served as a Public Affairs Officer for all the manned spaceflights of the Mercury and Gemini series. He also had occasion to participate in many other space and aeronautical events, seminars, and professional conclaves.

Major Sparks' formal military education, other than Flight Training, includes the Ballistic Missile Staff Orientation course, conducted at Vandenburg Air Force Base, California; the Space Operations course, Air University; the Squadrons Officers School, Air University; and Survival Training.

His civilian schooling has included attendance at the University of Tennessee, University of Alabama, Kansas University, University of Maryland, Washburn University, University of Houston, and St. Mary's University.

He has written several books related to aeronautics and astronautics, including *Rescue from the Air and in Space*, and *Winged Rocketry*.